D0981300

WORD PLAY

WORD PLAY

BY

JOSEPH T. SHIPLEY

HAWTHORN BOOKS, INC.

PUBLISHERS

New York

WORD PLAY

Copyright © 1972 by Joseph T. Shipley. Copyright under International and
Pan-American Copyright Conventions. All rights reserved, including the
right to reproduce this book, or portions thereof, in any form, except for the
inclusion of brief quotations in a review. All inquiries should be addressed to
Hawthorn Books, Inc., 260 Madison Avenue, New York, New York 10016.
This book was manufactured in the United States of America and published
simultaneously in Canada by Prentice-Hall of Canada, Limited, 1870 Birch-
mount Road, Scarborough, Ontario. Library of Congress Catalog Card Number: 78-150835.

Designed by Ellen E. Gal

3 4 5 6 7 8 9 10

For Daniel Vogel,
who has played
some of these with me

FOREWORD

This book is to help you have fun with words and playing word games. Some of the games you can play solo, some are good for two persons, some for larger groups. Some can be played while riding in a car.

Do not write in the book. You may want to try a puzzle or a problem on a friend, so keep the book clear of hints and answers. Whenever there's writing to do, have pen and paper ready. A pencil with an eraser is even better; then you can make changes if you wish.

When you know all the games, you can pass the book on to someone else. By that time you'll have your favorite word games and probably play them very well.

There are more games in this book than you can play in a month of Sundays. But we hope you'll enjoy reading about them and about how other people, some of them living thousands of years ago, also played them. And of course you can pick the ones that seem the most fun to you, and try them by yourself or with your friends. Everyone to his taste, as the old woman said when she kissed the cow.

Enjoy the games. You'll be surprised how much you learn while you're having fun.

And I hope you'll join me in thanking the publisher's editors for the painstaking care with which they helped make the material clear and correct and the book attractive.

J. T. S.

CONTENTS

WORD PLAY

1

RIDDLES, CONUNDRUMS, AND PUNS

The Riddle

Have you ever guessed a riddle? A riddle is a puzzling question that you have to figure out. It may have a trick in it. "From what can you take the whole, and have some left?" The answer is *wholesome*.

Riddles may be serious things. Lives have hung upon the answer. The Bible tells how Samson killed thirty men because of a riddle. He married a Philistine girl (not Delilah, she came later) and at the wedding feast gave the thirty guests a riddle. If they guessed it, the prize was a set of garments for each of them. They could not guess it, but they teased the answer out of his bride. When Samson saw he had been cheated, he killed thirty other Philistines and gave their garments to the wedding guests. Then the Philistines burned the bride's house, with her and her father inside.

Do you remember Samson's riddle?

Out of the eater came something to eat;
Out of the strong came something sweet.

That's a hard one! It becomes easier when you know that Samson had killed a lion (with his bare hands), and later found that bees had made a hive in the carcass and secreted honey.

Riddles were common among all ancient peoples. The Sphinx had one she gave to all comers. When they could not guess the answer, she killed them. When the Greek hero Oedipus gave her the right answer, she turned to stone. You can still see her in the desert near Cairo.

Here is the riddle of the Sphinx: "What is it that goes on four legs in the morning, on two legs at noon, and on three in the evening?" (1)*

Among many ancient peoples, including the Anglo-Saxons, riddles used to be given in poems. At the end of a feast, the gleeman, a kind of minstrel, would chant a song of their leader's great deeds or of the tribal hero. The warriors would interrupt to cheer, beating the rhythm on the table with their tankards of ale. Then the tribal poet would rise, and a sudden hush would reign in the long hall as they all listened eagerly to his poem, intent to solve the riddle.

About a hundred of the Anglo-Saxon riddles have been preserved—without the answers—and many of them are so tricky that scholars are still quarreling over the solutions. Here is part of a long but fairly simple one:

> Along the ground I grub, going as he guides me,
> The grey-haired foe of the forest, who is my head . . .
> Green upon one side is my going in,
> Swart upon the other surely is my path. (2)

You will notice that the Anglo-Saxon riddle is in the first person; the thing you have to guess describes itself. Here is a complete one:

> I am a noble being, known to earls,
> And I rest often with the high and the low,
> Famed among the folk. I fare widely.

---

*A number in parentheses indicates that the answer is after the same number at the back of the book.

With me, at times remote from friends,
Booty remains, when I glory in the burgs
And a bright course. Now learned men
Greatly love my presence. (3)

Not only were riddles a favorite game of the ancient tribes, but primitive peoples of today delight in solving them. Here is a simple riddle from Ethiopia:

What rises and sets
And never forgets? (4)

A more difficult Ethiopian riddle asks:

No matter how little you will it,
What multiplies when you kill it? (5)

Farther south in Africa, the riddle is usually fashioned not as a question but as a statement. Among the South African Venda tribe, for instance, they say:

The chief moves slowly
Among his waiting people. (6)

When they speak of "a place that reminds us to honor the chief," the Venda refer to a slippery spot after a rainfall, where to keep his balance a man has to bow.

From the South Caroline Islands, near the Philippines, comes the neat description:

Two sisters sit at the upstairs windows;
They look all around, but cannot see each other. (7)

Just a couple of generations ago, in Hawaii, the chieftains' sons were trained in the art of *hoopaapaa*, the riddle contest. This was a duel, with official judges, in which a contestant was given a riddle to solve; then he tried to top this with a trickier riddle for his opponent. Instead of fighting with swords or poisoned arrows, chiefs would stake their entire possessions, and sometimes even their lives, on their success in the riddle contest.

Here are some of the riddles from the Hawaiian contests:

1. Red above, red below, with a cheerful call.
2. Three walls and you reach water.
3. My house has one beam and two doors.
4. Dive and rise, dive and rise, and draw out.
5. Two pebbles looking at the earth and sky.
6. My misshapen melon hanging on a cliff. (8)

Nearer home, riddles have been caught in nursery rhymes. Everyone knows that Humpty Dumpty, who had a great fall and couldn't be put together again, is an egg. Here are three more of Mother Goose's riddles:

1. Little Nancy Etticoat
   With a white petticoat
   And a red nose;
   She has no feet nor hands;
   The longer she stands
   The shorter she grows.

2. A houseful, a hole full,
   You cannot catch a bowlful.

3. Two brothers we are; great burdens we bear,
   By which we are heavily pressed;
   The truth is to say, we are full all the day,
   And empty when we go to rest. (9)

Riddles can be enjoyed in three ways:

(1) Solo. Read them yourself, and try to figure out the answer.

(2) With one friend or a group. Read the riddle aloud. Your friend tries to figure out the answer. If there's a group, the first one tries. If he* can't solve it, the next in order tries. Score one point for a correct answer. One point off if he gives up. Zero

---

*He, when we use it in general, is to be thought of as including she. Our language has many gaps (see Chapter 8); one of them is the absence of a word to embrace both sexes. Therefore we say that, grammatically (as well as dramatically), the male embraces the female.

if he guesses and is wrong. (Scores count this way to encourage trying.)

(3) For a group. When you expect guests, write in advance a riddle on one sheet, the answer on another. Do this for as many riddles as you expect guests. Distribute the papers; each gets a riddle and an answer, but not the answer to his own riddle. In turn, each reads his riddle, and the one with the answer responds. If someone doesn't know he has the right answer, he should pay a forfeit. You can make up a forfeit when you need it. A favorite tells the loser to

> Nod to the wittiest,
> Bow to the prettiest,
> And kiss the one you love the best.

It's always interesting to see who are the three chosen. Maybe they're all one!

The Conundrum

Conundrums, the next variety of word game, can be played the same three ways as the riddle. In fact, a conundrum *is* a riddle, framed in the form of a question, with some form of word play in the answer. No word expert has been able to discover how it got its name.

Here is a batch of conundrums for you to riddle:

1. How far can you walk into the woods?
2. What should you keep after you give it to someone?
3. If you shoot at four birds on a branch and kill one, how many remain?
4. To what question should you always answer nothing?
5. What can be right but never wrong?
6. Why is necessity like an ignorant attorney?
7. What is the largest ant?
8. What is it you do to a cradle and eat for breakfast? (10)

Here are two riddles I remember from my boyhood Sunday school. They make a pair. "Why does no one have to starve in the desert?" "Because of the sand which is there." "And how came the sandwiches there?" "Ham went into the desert, and his descendants bred and mustered there."

Many conundrums are based on resemblances or differences. Here are a few:

1. What's the difference between a blind man and a sailor in prison?
2. What's the difference between a lone fisherman and a reluctant student?
3. What's the difference between a railroad conductor and a teacher?
4. What's the difference between a waiter who's just served bread and an angry goat?
5. Why is a baker like a poor man?
6. Why is a mouse like hay?
7. Why is coal not sold at the market? (11)

Often, when someone is asked a conundrum or other riddle, he has to say, "I give up." Then you give him the answer. W. S. Gilbert knew this too; in one of his musicals, *The Gondoliers,* he says:

> Hop and skip to fancy's fiddle,
> Hands across and down the middle,
> Life's perhaps the only riddle
> That we shrink from giving up.

The Pun

The use of one word in two senses is called a pun. Puns are double-tongued creatures; they seem to say one thing, then flash! we discover that they mean another.

Puns can be quite serious. Saying a thing that may have two meanings can be disastrous. A great Greek king went to the oracle to ask whether he should start a war. The oracle answered: "The result will make you happy." The king went to war—and was killed. He had not remembered the ancient wise man's saying: "Count no man happy until he is dead."

Puns have been popular at all times, and are found in many great books. In fact, the Catholic Church was founded on a pun. For Jesus said to Simon: "Thou art Peter, and upon this rock I will build my church." In the Greek, *petros* is the name for Peter and also the word for *rock*.

Shakespeare's plays are full of puns. They abound in his comedies, but they are found in his tragedies as well. In *Romeo and Juliet,* when the usually merry Mercutio has been fatally stabbed, he says: "Look for me tomorrow and you will find me a *grave* man." Lady Macbeth, taking the bloody daggers from her husband as he shrinks back after he has murdered the King, declares:

> I'll gild the faces of the grooms withal,
> For it must seem their guilt.

Later on, the three weird sisters play cruelly upon Macbeth by making double-tongued promises. They tell him he cannot be harmed until Birnam Wood comes to his castle. But the advancing troops break branches from the trees to carry before them as camouflage, and the sentry cries out that the forest is moving. A modern college cartoon added another pun to Shakespeare's word play, by making the sentry cry: "Cheese it, the copse!"

There was a Frenchman in the eighteenth century who boasted that he could pun on any subject. Someone called out, "The King." Without an instant's pause he responded: "The King is not a subject."

There have been punning contests. Jonathan Swift, who wrote *Gulliver's Travels,* was a great player of word games (some he invented we shall look at in Chapter 8). Swift had punning bouts with Thomas Sheridan, grandfather of Richard Brinsley Sheridan, who wrote the comedies *The School for Scandal* and *The Rivals.* Swift wrote *A Modest Defence of Punning;* three years later, in 1719, his friend Sheridan wrote a book called *The Art of Punning,* with thirty-four rules for becoming a good punster.

Several poems have been written, in German and French as well as English, with a pun in every line. Here is just a couplet from a long poem by Theodore Hook:

The dyer who by dying lives, a dire life maintains;
The glazier, it is known, receives his profits from his panes . . .

Of course, puns are mainly used for the less serious moments of living, although they appear in every field of life.
In the dairy business:

> You can't beat our milk, but you can whip our cream.

In art:

> "I see the horse you've drawn, but where is the wagon?"
> "The horse is supposed to draw that."

In the ministry:

> When the moths got at the minister's clothes, his wife said,
> "Let us spray."

On the river:

> When a boy went out for a row by himself, and his playmates
> started throwing stones toward him, he cried: "Don't rock the boat!"

In the ocean:

> There are so many birds offshore that often buoy meets gull.

On reaching shore:

> When the pious Pilgrims came safely to Plymouth Rock, they fell
> first upon their knees and then upon the aborigines.

In tourism:

> Everyone knows of the man who went to the seaside hotel for a rest
> and a change. The bellboy got the change, and the hotel got the rest.

In poetry: At the end of Thomas Hood's poem "Faithless Sally Brown," when the lover died,

> They went and told the sexton, and
> The sexton tolled the bell.

In proverbial wisdom:

> There is an old English saying: Take care of the pence, and the pounds will take care of themselves. Lewis Carroll, in *Alice in Wonderland*, tells us to take care of the sense, and the sounds will take care of themselves.

When an actor or a politician becomes unpopular, impetuous persons sometimes throw eggs at him. In the spring of 1970, eggs were thrown on the lawn of a Lancaster school in England, to demonstrate that eggs tossed onto grass are not likely to break, as they invariably do on concrete or your kitchen floor. Other schools scrambled to join the tossing, and even an airplane broke into the act—and one undergraduate was egged on by his ambition to compile a list of sixty egg puns, surely an eggsaustive survey.

Puns not only have a life of their own, but they slip into many word games. We have seen them in riddles and conundrums. They are sly in charades; they are bold in homonimbles; and they wink at you in the more devious definitions of crossword puzzles.

Although Sheridan said that the Roman god Janus, the two-faced god, may have been the originator of the pun, its origin is lost in prehistory. It goes back at least as far as the Garden of Eden. The Hebrew word *Adam* means *man*. And the Hebrew name for Eve, the first woman, means *talk*. Talk was impossible until woman came. And the first words spoken, jokesters tell us, were a form of word play, the palindrome (see Chapter 11): When Adam saw his rib come to separate life, he bowed politely and introduced himself: "Madam, I'm Adam."

Many people groan when they hear a pun. The habit of the groan has grown on us. Rule 32, in Sheridan's book, says: "Never speak well of another punster." The fact of the matter is that we groan because we didn't think of it first.

2

THE ANAGRAM TWISTERS:
PIEGRAMS, SCRABBLING,
GHOSTS, AND TARGETS
FOR THE HANGMAN

To analyze is to take something apart. It may be a chemical composition or an idea. You see what it is made of.

Gramma comes from the Greek root meaning *letter*. So to anagrammatize is to take a word apart. Sometimes you just scramble the letters, for someone else to put together again. Sometimes, out of the letters of a word, you make another word. Either way, you have an anagram.

Piegrams

There are many sorts of games played with anagrams. All over the world they are printed in newspapers, as a daily or a weekly challenge to the readers.

For instance, I found a newspaper in India that had a box headed "Today's Chaotic." Underneath was a scrambling of letters, which you had to turn into a word. One Tuesday, they printed this: SLICNAFATAT. Rearrange the letters and you'll find it is *fantastical*.

This is a game you can easily make up for yourself. Scramble any word you please, and give the mix-up to your friends. *Pie* —besides meaning the kind you eat—is the word for mixed-up printer's type. So we may call this sort of anagram a Piegram.

Some good words to scramble for pie are *longitude, perpendicular, encyclopedia.* You can choose any fairly long word. For a party, you might pie the name of a guest. The piegram SHIENLLWOWEN turns out to be *Helen Winslow.*

By the way, the pie you eat really got its name from the mix-up. The first meaning of pie was a bird, a kind of woodpecker. There are three varieties, the French pie, the rain pie, and the Margaret or magpie. The magpie likes to fill its nest with shiny articles. Many a country lady, missing a jewel from her dressing table near an open window, has had it recovered from a nearby magpie's nest. And from the mixture of items in a pie's nest, the word was applied to the mixture under a crust, the chicken pie, the mince pie, or the cherry pie. The Pied Piper got his name from the mixture of colors in his suit. An anagram is a letter pie.

Wordbreak

The most frequently played anagram game gives you a fairly long word, such as *collegiate,* and asks you to see how many smaller words you can make from its letters. This game appears in newspapers under various names; let us call it Wordbreak.

Usually, when a word is given to a group, the goal is to get the most words in five minutes. Another way of scoring is to have the one with the most words read his list. Everyone cancels a word he has when it is read. The one with the most words *no one else has* wins. (Take off one point for every word misspelled or not allowed. What is not allowed should be agreed upon in advance. For instance, no plurals, no foreign words, no proper names.)

Target

One variation of anagrams I found in a London paper is called Target, because it sets the target, the number of words you should aim at finding. For the example below: "fourteen words, good; sixteen words, very good; twenty words, excellent." This game allows words of four or more letters; one word must have ten letters; and every word must contain the letter in the big space. Here is a sample Target:

H	A	H	
M	O	P	**O**
T	O	E	

(12)

It is easy to make a target anagram. Just begin with any ten-letter word. Some you might use are *intriguing, antagonism, alliterate, marrowbone, pantomimes, rheumatism, stumblebum.* I have underlined the letter you might put in the big space, to be used in every word. When you select a ten-letter word for the game, make the box as in the sample, then try it yourself. After you have written all the words you can find, count them (including the original word), and make that number the "excellent" target.

Jumbles

Another anagram variation is called by various names in various newspapers. The most frequent term is Jumbles. Here is a jumble for you to solve:

YOLOCL	CONKK	GNIBE	TORAS
OO _ _ _ _	_ O _ O _	O _ _ _ _	OO _ _ _

There are four pied words for you to unscramble. Write the correct words on the line below, and the letters in the circles are a new scramble. In this jumble, the circled letters can be rearranged to name a kind of pipe. (13)

Here are two more jumbles:

1.

DUSTIP	CENUAN	TNECS	NIQUAT
O _ O _ _ _	O _ _ O _ _	_ OO _ _	_ _ OO _ _

The circled letters name a pest.

2.

SERUGO	LYWLOS	SPIEON	GRONOLID
O _ _ _ O _	_ _ O _ _ O	O _ O _ _ _	_ _ O _ O _ _ _

The circled letters make many-sided figures. (14)

If you want more jumbles, you can easily make them. Pick any word to be the final word. Then find four other words that among them have all the letters of the final word. Make circles for the letters you need and dashes for the others. Then pie the four words, and you have them ready for the players. Give a clue to the final word.

You can, of course, make a jumble with the final word spelling somebody's name.

WYOLLE	RESSAN	LERVOC	RAQUES
O _ _ O _ _	_ O _ O _ _	O _ O _ _ _	_ _ _ O _ _

Solve this jumble, and you have *Carolyn*. The words are *yellow, snares, clover, square*.

Addagrams

Another variation is the Addagram. This also is easy to make. Choose any word of eight to ten letters. Make a row of that many squares, and number them. Suppose you select the word *conjugate*. That gives you nine boxes:

```
   1  2  3  4  5  6  7  8  9
 ┌──┬──┬──┬──┬──┬──┬──┬──┬──┐
 │  │  │  │  │  │  │  │  │  │
 └──┴──┴──┴──┴──┴──┴──┴──┴──┘
```

Now you pick words, all the letters of which are in the base word. It doesn't matter if the same letter is used more than once; just make sure that every letter *is* used. You might, for *conjugate*, choose *jug, nougat, cane*. Then, for each of these words, you write the number of the box where each letter should go, with a clue to the word:

4,5,6—a container for liquids
3,2,5,6,7,8—a sweet paste candy
1,7,3,9—source of sugar (or, old man's support)
Total: how to analyze a verb.

Here's another one for you to try:

```
      1   2   3   4   5   6   7   8
    ┌───┬───┬───┬───┬───┬───┬───┬───┐
    │   │   │   │   │   │   │   │   │
    └───┴───┴───┴───┴───┴───┴───┴───┘
```

5,4,3—very cold water
1,6,7,2,8—rains heavily
Total: quite dear. (15)

Versigrams

A Versigram is still easier to make. Just take a line or a stanza from a poem, and pie some of the main words:

> This is the forest limpvera,
> the gnurimmur pines and the chokelms.

Of course, you should choose lines less familiar than this one about the forest primeval, with the murmuring pines and the hemlocks. Like these:

> A legten little giplolow
> Was miswigmn in the keal,
> A boy was ginlenek on a log
> Watching a traerg kneas. (16)

There are better poems, but I just made this one up. The next four lines are by Wordsworth:

> I wandered nyelol as a ducol
> That stalfo on high o'er slave and shill,
> When all at once I siped a drowc,
> A host of denolg faldosidf. (17)

Sentagrams

Still another form of anagram makes sentences into which the players must fit words made from the base word. Let us call them Sentagrams.

Take the word *versatile*. Pie it, and make words to fit into the sentences below. The dashes show the number of letters in the desired word. All the letters must be in the base word—this time, *versatile*. Give the players the main word, straight or pied. Then dictate the sentences, telling the number of dashes for each omitted word, or have them written out in advance.

1. If you _ _ _ _ in an _ _ _ _ way, you will have bad companions; it is still more _ _ _ _ to try to draw a _ _ _ _ over your conduct.
2. Do not pack your _ _ _ _ _ _ until the consulate has given you your _ _ _ _ to visit Russia. Then you may plan to go many a _ _ _ _ _ across the _ _ _ _ steppes. Do you expect to fly across the Atlantic or to _ _ _ _?
3. If you run fast in the race, you may _ _ _ _ _ all your _ _ _ _ _ _ behind.
4. Eat no more than a _ _ _ _ _ _ of _ _ _ _ _; but with the _ _ _ _ _ knife cut a large slice of _ _ _ _. This will _ _ _ _ _ off any fear that you may _ _ _ _ _ _.
5. Write with chalk on the _ _ _ _ _; then you can readily _ _ _ _ _ any mistakes. (18)

Anyone finished before the time is up should see how many other words he can form from the base word. Score as for wordbreak. Add all the points; highest wins. Many other words are dormant in *versatile*. (19)

Another way of playing sentagrams is to write a sentence with one or two words pied. Here are a few:

1. When the fat lady stood on the laces, she blinked her eyes.
2. He that is once vicedeed is always cussipious.
3. The best napyshsiic are Dr. Tied, Dr. Tique, and Dr. Mymarner.
4. To cheat is a teacher's function.
5. He's like an ocrahn, slayaw in the treaw and never learns to misw.
6. He that sloes his retpem is in the grown.
7. Tafcs are brutsnob things.
8. Cronas were dogo till beard was kedab.
9. One man's slierue is rhoanets ilto.
10. He that sendac till lytidhag will plees in colsho. (20)

You can easily make more of these yourself. Take any short sentence from a book or a newspaper, and pie a few key words. Try it with some of the proverbs in the last chapter.

Equagrams

You may have noticed that, in the first sentence of the *versatile* game, all four of the correct words had the same letters: e,i,l,v. There are many such letter shifts in our language; we can call them Equagrams. Inside *versatile,* besides the equagrams *evil, live, vile, veil,* you can find other sets, for instance, *eat, ate, tea, eta; vale, veal, lave; steal, teals, stale, slate, tales, least.*

You can work the same shift with some names. Do they pay high *taxes* in *Texas?* Don't *blame Mabel;* that will make her friend *Rose sore. Charles* walked in the grove of *larches.* Every italicized word in the following sentences can be rearranged to form a first name:

The *soil* was hard; he had to *lean,* then *tap,* on the *bat* to loosen the *yam.* But it was a *lark,* at the captain's *nod,* to *draw* a *map* of the *road* for the *army.* Celia and Alice should be good friends; their names are equagrams.

Sometimes a word can be broken, so that all its letters can be used to form two shorter words. From *stone,* besides the equagrams *onset, notes,* and *tones,* you can fashion: *so ten, net so, O nest, set on, no set.*

Here is a well-known but tricky shift: Make one word out of *new door.* Try that for a while. What you can make out of the letters of *new door* is the two-word combination *one word.* How long have such antics *continued unnoticed?* Do you go *aboard* ship or plane when you go *abroad?*

Here are some more words for equagrams. Use all the letters of the word to form other words. After each word is a possible number of shifts. Here's enough for a week when the TV is out of order. Take about five at a time:

1. draws (2)	10. slave (4)	19. depart (5)	28. pots (4)
2. idolatry (2)	11. aspired (9)	20. pears (9)	29. truce (3)
3. times (5)	12. result (6)	21. cats (3)	30. tables (5)
4. education (2)	13. priest (10)	22. drawer (4)	31. parts (3)
5. listen (4)	14. leap (3)	23. specter (2)	32. hatred (3)
6. mental (3)	15. lemons (2)	24. mean (3)	33. team (3)
7. general (2)	16. present (2)	25. forest (2)	34. instead (3)
8. plane (2)	17. crates (8)	26. spider (3)	35. scrape (3)
9. bizarre (1)	18. paternal (2)	27. realization (1)	36. exclaims (1) (21)

Try filling in these blanks with equagrams. Dashes show the number of letters:

1. The cook was at work in the _ _ _ _ _ _ _, trying to _ _ _ _ _ _ _ the sauce.
2. The public had a bad _ _ _ _ _ _ _ _ to the artist's _ _ _ _ _ _ _ _.
3. It finally _ _ _ _ _ _ _ _ _ _ his mind that he had made the wrong application, and he had to have his invention _ _ _ _ _ _ _ _ _ _.
4. The author had to _ _ _ _ _ _ _ _ _ some words in his dedication to please his _ _ _ _ _ _ _ _ _, who was paying to have his book published. (22)

Equagrams are by no means limited to English. They are known from ancient times, and have twisted their way into history. Of course you remember that Alexander the Great once lamented that there were no more worlds to conquer. That great Greek commander, however, might have gone back to Macedon in defeat if it were not for an equagram. He had been vainly trying to capture Tyre for so long that he decided to give up the siege and start back to Greece the next morning. That night he dreamed that he caught a satyr (in Greek, *satyros*). His oneirocritics (interpreters of dreams) were exultant. *"Satyros!"* they exclaimed. *"Sa Tyros!"* ("Tyre is his.") Alexander ordered a charge; the walls were breached, the city was taken, and his career as a conqueror was saved.

The Christians have similarly turned a Latin anagram to their triumph. When Pilate had Jesus before him, he asked the famous question: "What is truth?" In Latin, this is *Quid est veritas?* Its equagram, *Est vir qui adest,* means "It is the man who is here": Jesus.

Another serious use of the anagram was to get something on record and yet hide it from overly curious, envious, or hostile eyes. The great Renaissance scientist Galileo was tried by the Inquisition in 1632, and forced to take back his statement that the earth moved around the sun. So when he made some observations of the planet Venus, he hid his discovery in a Latin anagram thirty-five letters long.

The anagram has been put to other devious but practical uses. During World War I Arthur Brisbane, editor of Hearst's New York *Daily American,* suspected the *World* of stealing its

war news. His first edition, one day, announced the killing of
an Austrian colonel, Reflipe W. Thenuz. The dispatch also
appeared in a later edition of the *World*. The next morning,
Brisbane told this in an editorial, pointing out that there was
no such dispatch and no such person, the name being a phonetic
anagram of "We pilfer the news."

Hebrew and Arabic are among the languages that provide
many anagrams. And French. The French poet Gabriel Hécard
in 1821 wrote a poem of twelve hundred rhyming lines, every
one of which contains an equagram. How much French do you
know? Here is just one couplet, in which he tells

> *Que le dupeur est sans pudeur;*
> *Qu'on peut maculer sans clameur . . .*

Reversagrams

There are some words that form another word when read
backwards. You have already noticed how not to live (turn *live*
backwards). You can also reverse *part, denier, keel, leveler, rail,
rood, doom, spoons, smart, step, sloops, plug, lever, leper, loop,
desserts, repaid, warder, deliver, drawer, star, straw, pots, pans.*
Also *pot, pan, devil,* and *god.* Such words are Reversagrams.

You can easily make sentences, with dashes showing the
number of letters to be filled in by a pair of reversagrams. Then
give clues:

You can't cure _ _ _ _ _ by rubbing them with _ _ _ _ _.
Clues: You don't get them from toads; there's a man made
of it in *The Wizard of Oz.* (23)

A few words just say themselves over when you read them
backwards: *deified, rotator, eve, reviver, redder, noon, tenet,
deed, pep, peep, tot, toot, eke, radar.* There are also reversible
sentences; we call them palindromes; you can see them in Chapter 11.

Along with these belong the Demigrams, words of which the

second half repeats the letters of the first half, as *steppest, reappear, murmur, intestines, horseshoer.* A list of double or reduplicated words, like *tut-tut* and *fiddle-faddle,* is in Chapter 6.

Anapairs

Anapairs are a step-up variety of anagrams. Take some words that go together, like *rock* and *roll.* Pie one of the pair. Players must work out the pie—and write the partner. Here are just a few:

Pie: 1. beard; 2. rhedutn; 3. ledhail; 4. tujiel; 5. slacdermb; 6. nibro. (24)

Anacrostic

Another doubled variety of anagrams is Anacrostic. Here is one:

Pie: 1. norkbe; 2. memestios; 3. beltrire; 4. yonngain; 5. leetecnxl; 6. vyoell; 7. tracier.

When you have unscrambled the pies, you have still another pie —because the correct words must be rearranged so that their first letters spell a word. Clue for the initial word (the acrostic): a long-haired quartet whom Queen Elizabeth II made members of the Order of the British Empire. (25)

Here is another anacrostic:

Pie: 1. zayl; 2. kyop; 3. yeas; 4. peon; 5. kleind; 6. pepsoo; 7. claks; 8. drawne. Clue for initial word: the one that's always last. (26)

It is easy to make an anacrostic. First pick your word, say *peace.* Write its letters, one under the other. Next to each letter write a word beginning with that letter. Then pie these words. Like this, for example:

P	perchance	phencarec
E	entirely	trenyile
A	antlers	slarten
C	cunning	nnnguic
E	eastward	tradsawe

Then make up a clue for the initial word. A good clue for *peace* might be: what all the world wants. Give the players the pied words (in a different order) and the clue.

It is just as easy to make an anacrostic with a name. Unscramble these: *gnuoy, gnohilw, creamon, lyvole, resistin, nnddeeti, greeny.*

If you get the right words, then put them in the right order, the first letters will spell *Shirley.* Of course, I started with *Shirley* when I made this up. You can start with a friend's name, and make an anacrostic for his birthday.

Here are the unscrambled words for *Shirley: young, howling, romance, lovely, sinister, indented, energy.*

Pied Place Cards

When your friends come to the table at a party, they will be surprised if, instead of seeing their first names, they find pied letters on the place cards. They will have fun walking around, mentally unscrambling the names until they find their own place. Someone will probably call out: "I've found Edith!" (tidhe). A fifteen-year-old friend of mine did this for a party; she wrote me that it made a delightful part of the festivities.

There are anagrams that seem to fit one another; these may be called Aptagrams. Thus it seems fair to state that the *lumber industry duly runs timber;* to hear *Albert Einstein* declare *"I tear bent lines"*; to have his predecessor *Euclid,* the first great mathematician, claim: *"I led, U C."* Will you go to the *penitentiary*? *"Nay, I repent it."* The Beatles? *These bleat!* The U.S. Library of Congress: *It's only for research bugs.*

Notes are *tones. Evil* is *vile.* When the *telegraph* was invented, it was hailed as a *great help. Surgeon—Go, nurse! Lawyers: sly ware. Punishment: nine thumps. Sweetheart: there we sat. Received payment: every cent paid me. Constraint: cannot stir. Lowest: we lost. Alterations: neat tailors. Train: it ran. Regulating: get a ruling. French Revolution: violence run forth.*

Perhaps the most remarkable aptagram is the one about *Washington crossing the Delaware: he saw his ragged Continentals row.* Somebody had a lot of patience to figure that out.

Astronomers has both an aptagram, *moonstarers,* and an antigram, *no more stars.*

The philologist in Christopher Hampton's hit play *The Philanthropist* (opened in London in 1970, in New York in 1971) fashions anagrams at the drop of a chat. His *"Make the real shapes"* contains the name of the greatest English dramatist and of his best-known play.

Anagrams

If you go to a store and ask for Anagrams, you will get a box of little cardboard or wooden squares, each marked with a letter. If you are patient, you can, of course, cut your own squares out of cardboard. Make more of the letters that are used more often.

There is no established frequency of the recurrence of the twenty-six letters in English words, because different counts have included or omitted technical terms, the various parts of verbs, and other special cases. The three or four suggested lists vary slightly. The one used by cryptographers who try to break codes by frequency is as good as any. Here it is: ETAONIRSH DLUCMPFYWGBVJKQXZ. You'll make no mistake in assuming that *e* is used some ten times as often as *z.*

This game of anagrams is most fun with two to six players. Shuffle all the squares on a table, blank side up. Each player picks five letters, which the others do not see. Then the first player picks a letter from the remaining ones. If, with three or more of the letters he now holds, he can make a word, he puts that word in front of him, facing the other players. Then he discards a letter, putting it face up in the center of the table. If he cannot make a word, he just discards a letter. (If he has made a word using all his letters, he picks another, and uses it or discards it.) The next player repeats the process, and so around, each ending by discarding a letter face up.

If any letter a player has (or a discarded letter, or both) can be used, with all the letters of a word in front of another player, to make a new word, he can, when his turn comes, take the word from the other player and make the new word of his own. (Usual rules: just adding *s* or *ed* doesn't count.)

A word may in this manner change hands several times in a game. If a player, for example, has the word *bad*, you can make it *bard*. (And, while you cannot add *s* to make *bards*, you can make the new word *brads*.) Or *bad* can become *bead*. But *brad* or *bead* can become *bread* (or *beard*). If in your hand or on the table there is an *o*, and you pick an *r*, you can change *bread* to *boarder* (or *broader*). In this way, your quickness in finding words combines with your luck in picking the letters you need.

Play until all the letters have been turned face up. Score: one point for every word you have. Then one point for every letter more than five in a word. Thus *boarder* will give you one for the word, plus two for the extra letters.

Scrabblings

Closely allied to anagrams is Scrabble. This game provides you with a board, and you have to build words on its squares, always building on what is already there. Every letter has a value marked on it, and some squares are marked for double or triple points. You start with seven letters in front of you, and after every play you pick enough to have seven again. Once a word is set on the board, the order of the letters cannot be changed; you must build on what is there. You add to your own the value of the letters on the board that you use. For example:

You can add *se* after the *ten*. Then the last *e* can be built to *even*. Now the board may have this pattern:

```
        ┌───┐
        │ M │
    ┌───┼───┼───┬───┐
    │ T │ E │ N │ S │ E │
    └───┼───┼───┴───┼───┤
        │ N │       │ V │
        ├───┤       ├───┤
        │ U │       │ E │
        └───┘       ├───┤
                    │ N │
                    └───┘
```

If, instead of *even*, the word is *ever,* you can get several words by adding *oan* across the top, making

```
        ┌───┬───┬───┬───┐
        │ M │ O │ A │ N │
    ┌───┼───┼───┼───┼───┤
    │ T │ E │ N │ S │ E │
    └───┼───┼───┴───┼───┤
        │ N │       │ V │
        ├───┤       ├───┤
        │ U │       │ E │
        └───┘       ├───┤
                    │ R │
                    └───┘
```

This will give you all the points for *moan, on, as,* and *never.* You cannot add like this, of course, unless every combination of adjacent letters forms a word.

You must keep on the alert for tricky combinations like these. You should also try to place your words on squares that will not give the next player an easy chance to land on an extra-point square. Some players even let a chance for a word go by, rather than help the next player to some extra points. That's what they call finesse. It's part of the game in scrabble.

Scrabble is a combination of anagrams and word squares. More squares are in Chapter 11.

You can buy similar games in the shape of playing cards, with one letter on a card. Still others give you several dice, with six letters on each die. You deal or pick the cards or toss the dice, and try to form words with the letters fortune sends you.

Ghosts

Perhaps the most popular word-building game is Ghosts. This needs no equipment and is played orally. The first player says a letter, the next adds another, building toward a word of four or more letters but trying not to end a word. If you end a word, you are "dead," and the next player starts a new one. When a player is "dead" three times, he becomes a "ghost" and drops out of the game. When all but one are ghosts, the survivor is the winner. (Sometimes it is a rule that anyone that speaks to a ghost becomes one.)

You should figure in advance, trying to make sure that a word does not end with you. Thus, if the letters up to you are *trib,* instead of saying *e* you can build toward *tribal,* or *tribute,* or *tributary.* You must have a word in mind. Count around to make sure it doesn't come back and "kill" you.

If you cannot think of a word, you may challenge the player before you. If he can give a word with his letters, you are dead; if he cannot, he is dead.

Double Ghosts

A trickier form of the game allows you to add a letter to either end. Each player gives all the letters before his plus his own. For example: l. l–i. l–i–e. k–l–i–e. c–k–l–i–e. c–k–l–i–e–s. i–c–k–l–i–e–s. u–i–c–k–l–i–e–s. u–i–c–k–l–i–e–s–t. The next player is caught dead with the *q.*

Other rules are the same as for one-way ghosts.

Hangman

Another word-building game that may "kill" you is Hangman. This is played only by two. Think of a word. Put on paper as many dashes as the word has letters. Your opponent guesses a letter. If it is in the word, you write it over the appropriate dash. If not, you start to build a gallows to hang your opponent. You draw one line at a time, which—as you can see on the figure below—allows him fifteen wrong guesses before he is hanged. If you're generous, you can put in two eyes, a mouth, and a belly button, allowing nineteen wrong guesses. That's over two-thirds of the alphabet; he should figure out the word before then!

If he gets hanged, you tell him the word. Then he tries to hang you. The one that guesses the most words, or the fewest wrong letters, wins.

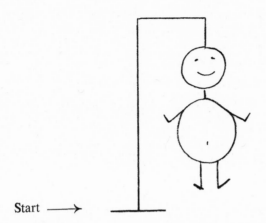

Start ⟶

Let's get ahead before we're hanged! The anagram family makes a *taf trephac!*

3

ALPHABET PARADE:
LETTER WORDS,
SPELLING, THE REBUS,
AND STOPS

The possible combinations of the twenty-six letters of the English alphabet are approximately 40,329,146,112,660,563,558,-400,000,000. Give or take a few billion, that's quite a number!

Fewer than 700,000 of these possible combinations have been used as words in our language. So there are many more words lying around, waiting for someone to invent them. Some possible new words are hunted in Chapter 8.

But some words can be made of just a single letter. As a matter of fact, more than half our letters have the sound of a word. What letter is 1. an insect; 2. an article; 3. a drink; 4. a vegetable; 5. in your head; 6. an exclamation; 7. another exclamation (or to be in debt); 8. a body of water (or behold); 9. a bird; 10. a yard and a quarter; 11. a hint; 12. the person spoken to; 13. unknown; 14. the reason; 15. a printer's measure; 16. another printer's measure; 17. what letter says things exist? (27)

Most of the twenty-six, also, can be used in "letter words," combinations of letters that sound like words. Ask your friends which letters (the number shows how many) make words for which these are the clues:

1. a foe (3)
2. too much (2)
3. go to ruin (2)
4. you notice (2)
5. attempt a composition (2)
6. title of an ambassador (4)

7. This is not hard (2)
8. jealousy at another's success (2)
9. convenience (5)
10. surpass (2)
11. below freezing (2) (28)

Then there's the classical remark of the woman who found no milk in her container. What did she say to it, in seven letters? (29)

Read the following; your great-grandfather may have puzzled over it (30):

Y Y U R Y Y U B,
I C U R Y Y 4 me.

You can always hope to live and learn.

Here are a few more questions about our letters:

1. Why is *A* like noon?
2. Why is *H* good for deafness?
3. Why is *O* the noisiest vowel?
4. Why is *D* like a bad boy?
5. A three-letter word of one syllable; add a letter and it has three syllables. What's the word?
6. The same, with a word of four letters?
7. The same, with a word of five letters?
8. What starts with a T, ends with a T, and is full of T?
9. The author of *Alice in Wonderland,* in a letter to a girl, wrote: "With the first seven letters of the alphabet, I can make a word." She couldn't. Can you? (31)

How many words can you think of, like *cab,* containing only letters adjacent in the alphabet? A letter may be used more than once in a word. Two points for a two-letter word, three points for three, five points for four, ten points for five, and twenty points for six letters. One hundred is an excellent score. (32)

Alphabeteasers

Try to write sentences in which each word begins with the next letter in the alphabet. Some have been written twenty-six words long, from *A* to *Z,* but they never seem to make much sense. You can do better with a smaller number. Tell your friends to write a telegram—ten words—each word in alphabetical succession, starting with any letter they choose. See who can write the most amusing message. Here's one, starting with *C:*

Call dependable expert, first grade. Henry in jail, klepto-mania. Love. (I began with *C* so that I could end with *Love.*)

Number Letters

Letters not only can stand for words, they can represent those very special words we call numbers. In many languages, including ancient Greek and Hebrew, you count by letters. The Hebrew goes up the alphabet: *aleph* is one, *beth* is two, *gimel* three, and so on. In all the Western world, until after the tenth century (when we borrowed the Hindu signs from the Arabs) Roman numerals were used, which are letters: I is one; V is five; X is ten; L is fifty; C is one hundred; D is five hundred; M is one thousand. We still use these letters, on buildings and some-times on the face of clocks. And some English words consist entirely of number letters: DIM, MIX, MIMIC, MILD, LIVID, CIVIL. If you want, make clues for these and give them to your friends. With the clue, tell them the number of letters.

Here is a mixture. What name has five hundred at the beginning and at the end, five in the middle, the first letter and the first number in between? (33)

Another sort of number word makes a game. Take three minutes to write as many words as you can containing the sound or the spelling of the numbers from one to ten. Think of one for each number first, then try for more. Score ten points if you have a word for all ten numbers, one point for each word more. Such as:

wonderful, one-sided, won
tool, toothache, twosome
threefold, threnody
fortify, fortune, foursome
fiver, five-finger, five-penny (nail), five-star
sixty, six-shooter
seventy, seven-league boots
eighty, concentrate, educate, state
ninepins, ninefold, benign
tennis, tenderfoot, discontent, tenfold

A Dozen to Say

There is an old song telling what "my true love gave to me" on each of the twelve days of Christmas. And a game has been made of the first twelve numbers, to be played by two, three, four, six, or twelve players. Each player is assigned numbers, using all from one to twelve. Then every player writes a description of something or someone for each of his numbers, every word beginning with the same letter as the number. The first player reads his words for number one. The next player repeats them, then reads his for two. Next player repeats both, then reads his for three. And so on. Any player forgetting words drops out, until only one is left. It's a hard job to get through all twelve.

Here is a sample series:

One old Oxford ox opening oysters.
Two toads totally tired trying to trot to Toledo.
Three thick thumping tigers taking toast to tea.
Four finicky fishermen fishing for finny fish.
Five frippery Frenchmen foolishly feeding fat frogs.
Six sportsmen soberly shooting silver snipe.
Seven spotted salmon savagely swallowing shrimp.
Eight eminent Englishmen eagerly examining Europe.
Nine neighborly nincompoop noblemen nimbly nibbling nectarines.
Ten tinkering tinkers testily tinkering ten twinkling tentacles.
Eleven Eurasian elephants elegantly equipped.
Twelve typographical topographers typically transposing tempting types.

In one game I played, the finale was not only a topper but a stopper: "Twelve triumphant trumpeters triumphally trumpeting throughout the tragical tribulation tempting tenderfoots tied to tenterhooks." Not even a sword-swallower has a gullet to hold all those numbers!

The only passage in literature to match this as a memory game is the celebrated nonsense made up back around 1740 by Samuel Foote as a challenge to the actor Charles Macklin, who had boasted that he could memorize anything on hearing it once. How much of what Foote dashed off can you keep in your mind?

> So she went into the garden to cut a cabbage leaf to make an apple pie, and at the same time, a great she-bear coming up the street pops its head into the shop. What! No soap! So he died; and she very imprudently married the barber: and there were present the Picninnies, and the Joblilies, and the Garyulies, and the grand Panjandrum himself, with the little round button at top. And they all fell to playing the game of catch as catch can, till the gunpowder ran out of the heels of their boots.

Rebus

We have seen how a letter may stand for a word. On the other hand, sometimes a picture may stand for a letter. Even the position of something on the page may make it stand for the whole or part of a word. We call such a device a rebus. *Rebus* is a Latin word meaning *with things*. This kind of writing was known to the ancients; indeed, it is the basis of Egyptian hieroglyphics and other alphabets, including the Chinese symbols. In the Renaissance, nobles used this pattern in devising their coats of arms, and many a merchant put out a rebus sign. A man named Abel might begin his sign with a picture of a bell. The old English tavern the Bacchanals was mispronounced by the squires who drank there, and finally put up for its sign a bag o' nails. In Denmark today, you can tell a bakery because outside it is hanging a gilded pretzel; outside the barber shop is a basin. In Paris, a gilt horsehead shows a butcher shop that specializes in horse meat.

In games, while pictures are used, position is very important. How would you read the following? (34)

1.   stand   take   to   takings
            I   U   throw   my

2. Or this, which was on an envelope sent by mail?

                        Hill
                        John
                        Mass

3. Here's a piece of sound counsel to bring peace to a household:

                          B
          faults man quarrels wife faults

4. Or this description of an enamored man:

                          L
                         AF
                          D

The French enjoy this sort of game and have come up with one of the neatest rebuses of all. What's the shortest way of writing "I'm hungry" in French? *Ga!* (Capital *G,* small *a;* in French, *G grand, a petit,* which is pronounced just like *J'ai grand appétit:* "I'm hungry!")

The rebus—a thing for an idea—has been commonly used in real life. When gadabout Prince Hal assumed the throne as Henry V of England, the Dauphin of France sent him a barrel of tennis balls. This meant, "Go back to your games, and leave government to your betters." Henry responded to the insult by conquering France. Two thousand years earlier, when the Emperor Darius approached their land, the Scythians sent him a bird, a mouse, a frog, and five arrows. Darius was told this meant: "Fly away like a bird, hide your head in a hole like a mouse, or swim back across the river like a frog; or in five days you will be laid low by Scythian arrows." Darius responded by driving the Scythians out of their land.

And what is a wedding ring but a rebus? What is a birthday present but a pleasant way of saying "I love you, and wish you well"? In many ways, we use things to express our feelings. Such silence truly speaks louder than words.

Spelling

Man is the only creature on earth that can set down thoughts in writing. It follows (alas!) that man is the only creature troubled with spelling.

Some people just decide to disregard the problem, like my young nephew who said that when he grew up he wouldn't have to spell; he'd dictate to a secretary. And now that's just what he does.

Others, like the playwright Bernard Shaw, make fun of our tangles. Shaw said that *g–h–o–t–i* spells fish. Pronounce *gh* as in *rough, o* as in *women, ti* as in *notion.* What a notion! When Shaw died, he left his fortune for the establishment of a method of simplified spelling. The British Parliament ruled that his will was invalid.

Through the years, some simplifications in spelling have developed. The old *shoppe* is now usually called a *shop.* Americans leave the *u* out of most words like *honour* and *labour.* Shakespeare's spelling is frequently modernized in new editions. But on the whole, spelling tends to stick. It troubles many people but is wrapped into the history of words.

Some writers of grammars have tried to set up rules for spelling—"*i* before *e,* except after *c,*" and that sort of thing. But it's often more trouble to learn the rules—and the exceptions to the rules—than to tackle the separate words.

Here's one challenge: *-able* or *-ible?* Add the correct ending to these starters:

> *permiss- , charit- , convert- , excus- , indel- , incompat- , indispens- , perish- , intellig- , practic- , vener- , infall- , tang- , credit- , inevit- , aud- , comfort- , fashion- , mov- .*

To check, look these up in the dictionary, *after* you have written down your guesses. Then pore over these:

1. What word is spelled wrongly when it's right?
2. How many words can you think of that end with *-dous?*
3. Write two words that end *-chion*

4. Three words that end -*cion*
5. Four words that end -*shion*
6. Five words that end -*gion* (35)

There are a dozen or so each, for the endings -*lion, -nion, -pion,* and -*xion*. The -*sion* words can be counted by the scores, and the -*tion* words by the hundreds. Other endings are discussed in Chapter 12.

Here's a quick spelling check to try on your friends. Ask them: "How do you spell *joke?*" Then ask them to spell "*broke.*" "*Folk.*" "The white of an egg." The chances are they'll say *y–o–l–k.* Then you point out that the yolk is the yellow. We usually just say "the white" of an egg, but there is a word for it. The white of an egg is spelled *g–l–a–i–r.*

Paired Words

By sheer accident, some quite different words have the same sound or even the same spelling. When these are used in a sentence, you can readily tell them apart. No one is likely to confuse the animal *bear* with the *bear* that means to *carry,* or with the *bare* that means you haven't any clothes on. (There is even a song about these, telling that "the bear went over the mountain, with a little bear behind.") *Bore* and *boar, faint* and *feint*—there are hundreds of such pairs in the language. There are even triplets: *holy, holey, wholly* (sounds like a hymn!); *borough, burro, burrow* (do you dig?). We call such partners homonyms, which means "alike names." We can be even more technical and call the words spelled alike homographs, the words spelled differently but sounded alike, homophones. If they are spelled alike but differ in both sound and meaning (*sow* seeds, and the hog's girl friend, *sow*), they are heteronyms. You don't have to remember these technical terms; homonym covers them all. We'll look at the words themselves in Chapters 6 and 7.

In the meantime, here are some unpaired words that may trouble you. Write down the one misspelled word in each horizontal line. Try only ten at a time. If a word is new to you, hunt it in the dictionary.

A

1. piteous	malleable	copeous	malignant
2. paradise	paprika	polute	possess
3. sensible	sivility	censorious	centipede
4. conceited	congregate	confederacy	confedential
5. regenerate	regretable	refrigerator	recipe
6. trivial	triplicate	innocent	triumphent
7. sluvenly	slippery	sleuth	sluice
8. stammering	strategy	stalactite	strident
9. apparent	aptitude	apology	apreciate
10. intensely	inclusive	instagate	indemnity

B

1. electricity	elevation	elegible	ellipse
2. suppress	substitute	sympathize	supena
3. dipthong	dignified	diplomatic	devastate
4. pheasant	phisique	philanthropist	phlegmatic
5. pieces	pier	pickerel	picnicing
6. audience	audacious	audable	austere
7. ventriliquism	ventilate	venturesome	vengeance
8. sacrifice	religion	sacreligious	sacred
9. foreign	fortified	forfiet	formidable
10. cheiftain	chicanery	chivalrous	chestnuts

C

1. vile	vestibule	civilian	villian
2. ecstacy	constancy	ecclesiastic	eclipse
3. sieve	mischief	reciever	reimburse
4. obstruct	abreviate	abstract	absorbent
5. architect	arithmetic	archives	architype
6. knapsack	hunchback	bivouack	counterattack
7. submit	comitted	conduit	diameter
8. mutineer	mutible	mutilate	mutual
9. cite	pneumonia	tuberculosis	laringytis
10. siege	sieve	sinecure	sieze (36)

Spelling Bee

The spelling bee was very popular in colonial days, when each small town had gatherings for various community projects, from building a schoolhouse to husking the harvest corn. At a cornhusking bee, it was a young man's privilege to kiss the girl with a red ear (of corn).

The spelling bee is best played with a fairly large group. It is still popular in schools, for schoolwide or even citywide competition.

Two captains pick their teams, which line up on opposite sides. The umpire has a list of words. He reads one, either tells its meaning or uses it in a sentence, and repeats the word. The first player spells it.

The umpire waits to see whether anyone on the opposing team challenges. If so, the challenger spells the word, and the player who is wrong sits down. If there is no challenge and the word was spelled wrongly, the umpire spells the word, but no one sits down. (Some play a different rule: the umpire goes on mowing players down until somebody spells the word correctly.) The umpire then gives the next word to the next player on the opposite team. Continue until only one player is left standing. He is the champion.

Here are some words to try on your friends—if they'll let you —or at a spelling bee. But keep in mind the old Latin motto: "Nothing too much."

fierce	accommodate	grief	gazetteer
mischief	neither	rein	abridge
brief	palliate	impecunious	foreclosure
fricasseed	toboggan	xylophone	portable
accessible	believe	beguile	foment
omniscient	luxuriant	gnash	predilection
irascible	dinghy	mausoleum	weight
height	niece	harass	embarrassment
sciatica	fuchsia	accomplice	scoundrelly
hackneyed	alimentary	mountebank	cassowary
aperture	controversy	precedence	dilute
labyrinth	gaudy	optometry	pediatrician
relieve	synthesis	repetition	protein
eatable	sovereign	gusset	adversity
fiery	flaccid	turbulence	ceiling
untenable	insatiable	voracious	optimistic
apparel	diphtheria	veracious	whippoorwill
confectionery	sizable	tortoise	seizable
demurrer	amethyst	chamois	raiment
vindicate	acquiesce	already	bicycle
auxiliary	zealous	whether	yacht
tendency	unique	recommend	precious
license	jewelry	endorsement	efficient
dependent	defendant	character	occurrence
gnawing	guarantee	prevalent	receipt

Plurality

Some languages have what is called a dual number, a special form to be used when referring to two of a kind. English has only two forms: for one of a kind, and for more than one— singular and plural. It would be singular indeed if you had no trouble with the plural. The general rule, as we all know, is to add *s* or *es,* but there are many exceptions, and sometimes there's a problem as to where to put the *s.* You may speak of your brothers-in-law, for instance, but how would you refer to the brigadier general, if there are several?

Dictate (ten at a time) the following words, pausing after each, while the players write the plural:

> 1. embryo; 2. taxi; 3. it; 4. the years from 1960 through 1969; 5. brigadier general; 6. notary public; 7. madame; 8. beau; 9. Fanny; 10. monkey; 11. money; 12. myself; 13. alibi; 14. gallows; 15. deer; 16. fish; 17. genus; 18. genius; 19. ox; 20. fox; 21. titmouse (which is a bird); 22. species; 23. inspector general; 24. goose; 25. mongoose; 26. testatrix; 27. opus; 28. soprano; 29. sheaf; 30. datum; 31. criterion; 32. electron; 33. amoeba; 34. axis; 35. gross; 36. L; 37. wolf; 38. phenomenon; 39. bison; 40. fleet; 41. hero; 42. staff; 43. larva; 44. mosquito; 45. brother; 46. passerby. (37)

Speaking of plurals, do you know the difference between a plurality and a majority?

Can you write the seven English words that form their plural by changing the vowel? Two are parts of the body; five are of the animal kingdom. (38)

Punctuation

Punctuality, they say, is the thief of time. Or is that procrastination? Take the first letters of the one, and the last letters of the other, and you have something on which many persons have spent a lot of time: punctuation.

Some writers prefer not to bother with it. James Joyce, who took a lot of trouble to give us word trouble, wrote the last thirty-two pages of his novel *Ulysses* without one punctuation mark. It is printed that way, too. It is indeed a novel novel. Another writer put a batch of punctuation marks at the end of his book, and told his readers to tuck them in wherever they wished. But what would you do with sentences like these?

1. Time flies you cannot they fly so fast
2. That that is is that that is not is not that that is not is not that that is
3. Frank where Henry had had had had had had had had had had had had the teacher's approval (39)

In one of the earliest English comedies, about 1530, Ralph Roister Doister's message is read:

> Sweet mistress, whereas I love you nothing at all;
> Regarding your substance and riches chief of all;
> For your personage, beauty . . .

Bewildered at the woman's rage, the illiterate Ralph returns to the scribe, who innocently reads to him:

> Sweet mistress, whereas I love you; nothing at all
> Regarding your substance and riches; chief of all
> For your personage, beauty . . .

leaving Ralph more bemused than before.

A slip in punctuation once cost Uncle Sam a lot of money, by letting in free of duty some goods that were to have been taxed. By the time Congress could get around to amending the law, that slip had become known as "the twelve million dollar comma."

The presence of the comma might keep a smile from turning

into a frown, at the remark: "Women are pretty, generally speaking."

Here is a combination of letter words and punctuation marks in a rebus (40):

> If the B mt put:
> If the B. putting:

And now this chapter comes to a full stop.

4

PANGRAMS, ALPHABETTORS,
LIPOGRAMS—THE LONGER
THE SHORTER

What word contains all the twenty-six English letters? Of course, *alphabet!*

Persons learning to typewrite want to practice with sentences that use every letter of the alphabet. The usual sentence given in the United States is "The quick brown fox jumps over the lazy dog." This has thirty-five letters.

Even before the typewriter, it was a game to try to make the shortest possible sentence using all the letters. A hundred and fifty years ago, this one was offered: "John P. Brady, give me a black walnut box of quite fair size." This has forty-six letters.

An Irish cipher expert in World War I sent home this request: "Pack my box with five dozen liquor jugs." He never got them, but he cut the alphabet sentence down to thirty-two letters. His remained the shortest until, in 1964, the *Saturday Review* offered ten pounds of soda crackers for a shorter one.

Blowzy frights vex, and jump quick.
Waltz, nymph, for quick jigs vex Bud.

Each of these has twenty-eight letters, repeating *u* and *i.* I prefer the second, because I'd like to waltz with a nymph, and my nickname happens to be Bud.

Such letter packs have been called Pangrams, *pan* meaning *all.* In one of the verses of the Bible (Ezra 7:21) every letter of the alphabet is used, if you count *j* and *i* as one as they did in 1611, when the King James version of the Bible was printed.

Another pangram game seeks words containing all the five vowels. Are there such words? *Unquestionably!*

It's not really hard to list words with all five vowels. Set your friends to seeing how many they can jot down in three minutes. (41)

The next two hunts are harder:

1. How many words have all five vowels in alphabetical order? (42) All five vowels occur in reverse order in *uncontinental.*

2. With how few consonants can you make a word containing all five vowels? Not counting names and technical terms, the best the English language can come up with is a great old tree, with two consonants. Or what the cats did, at their convention. The French have a bird of a word, with only one consonant. (43)

It is interesting to note that every one of the vowels makes a word between the same pair of consonants: *pat, pet, pit, pot, put.* These are all with the short sound of the vowel. You can come near doing it with the long vowels: *pate, peat, pint* or *plight, potent* or *potation, repute* or *putative.* With *c* or *k* and *n* you can fit nine of the ten sounds: *can, ken, kin, con, cunning, cane, keen, kine, cone, coon.* Any other three-letter vowel catchers? Try for yourself. *Dan* will carry you a way. Also *last.*

It's easier if you try only the long vowel sounds; you should get at least six consonants that begin one-syllable words with each of the five long vowels. (44)

Alphabettor

A pervasive problem is to use all the letters of the alphabet in one fell swoop of associated words. In James Joyce's *Finnegans Wake,* which is a long, long play on words in seven tongues, there are two alphabet runs. One goes from *apple, bacchante, custard,* on to *Xray, yesplease,* and *zaza.* The other is a list of girls' names, beginning Ada, Bett, Celia. But before Joyce, a poet rejoiced to make an alphabet verse with lines like these:

> A is my Amy, so slender of waist;
> B's little Bet, who my button replaced . . .
> J is the Judy Punch finds to his taste . . .
> S is brisk Sal, who a chicken can baste . . .

A whole book of comic alphabets was gathered, in 1961, by that assiduous and seldom acidulous student of words, Eric Partridge.

The best-known alphabet verse is "The Siege of Belgrade," in which every word on the line begins with the appropriate letter. Here it is:

> An Austrian army, awfully arrayed,
> Boldly by battery besieged Belgrade.
> Cossack commanders cannonading come,
> Dealing destruction's devastating doom.
> Every endeavor engineers essay
> For fame, for fortune, forming furious fray;
> Gaunt gunners grapple, giving gashes good;
> Heaves high his head heroic hardihood.
> Ibrahim, Islam, Ismail, imps in ill,
> Jostle John, Jarovlitz, Joe, Jack, Jill,
> Kick kindling Kutosoff, kings' kinsmen kill.
> Labor low levels loftiest, longest lines,
> Men march 'mid mobs, 'mid mounds, 'mid murd'rous mines.
> Now nightfall's near, now needful nature nods,
> Opposed, opposing, overcoming odds.
> Poor peasants, partly purchased, partly pressed,
> Quite quaking, Quarter! Quarter! quickly quest.
> Reason returns, recalls redundant rage,
> Saves sinking soldiers, softens seignors sage.

Truce, Turkey, truce! Truce, treacherous Tartar train!
Unwise, unjust, unmerciful Ukraine!
Vanish, vile vengeance! Vanish, victory vain!
Wisdom wails war, wails warring words. What were
Xerxes, Xantippe, Ximenes, Xavier?
Yield, youth; yield, yeomen, yield your youthful yest,
Zealously, Zarius, zealously zeal's zest,
And all, allied, amicably advance abreast.

The repeated use of the same first letter is called alliteration; it chimes briefly at the end of Chapter 9.

You can make several sorts of alphabettors yourself. Limit your choice of words—for instance, name only things on or in the earth. Thus:

A is for artichokes, asphalt, and ants,
B is for bushes, bananas, and bugs,
C is for coconuts, cotton, and corn,
D is for diamond, dandelions, and dirt,
E is for ebony, elephants, and eggs,
F is for flowers, foxes, and fleas,
G is for goldenrod, gorillas, and geese,
H is for hyacinths, horses, and hogs,
I is for iris, and iron, and ice,
J is for jonquils, jackasses, and jugs,
K is for kangaroo, kapok, and kail,
L is for lilacs, and lynxes, and lambs,
M is for mahogany, mockingbirds, mint,
N is for needles, narcissus, and nests,
O is for olives, orioles, and ore,
P is for potatoes, pigments, and pears,
Q is for quagmire, quicksand, and quail,
R is for radishes, ruby, and rose,
S is for sunflower, serpent, and snail,
T is for tangerine, termites, and tar,
U is for uranium, umbles, and umber,
V is for vermin, vanilla, and violets,
W is for walnuts, weasels, and wax,
X is for xeranthemum, xenon, x-rays,
Y is for yogurt, yeast, yam, yaks, and yew (and you),
Z is for zebra, zinc, zircon, and zoo.

When you try this with a group, one word for each letter is enough. See who gets through first. Wait for the others, then each in turn read his list.

A neater trick is a double Alphabettor. Write the letters in a column down the center of the paper. To the left of each write a pleasant word; to the right, an unpleasant one. Like this:

agile	A	asinine
brainy	B	backward
clever	C	clumsy
desirable	D	diabolical
excellent	E	erratic
friendly	F	finicky
gracious	G	griping
harmonious	H	horrid
ingenious	I	impatient
jocund	J	juvenile
keen	K	knackless
lovely	L	lackadaisical
merry	M	meddlesome
nice	N	negligent
orderly	O	offensive
peerless	P	prying
qualified	Q	quarrelsome
reliable	R	repulsive
super	S	square
thoughtful	T	tiresome
unbiased	U	underhand
valiant	V	vain
warm-hearted	W	wasteful
xenial	X	xenophobic
youthful	Y	yowling
zippy	Z	zero

There are, of course, many others, as your ingenuity (and the dictionary) may provide them.

Phony Alphabet

Another alphabettor can run along the twenty-six letters for their sound. *Phon-* is a root meaning *sound;* a telephone *sounds far.* So we can call this a Phony Alphabet. If you're in a good humor, it can be a funny phony alphabet. Here's one for a taste. Remember, the sound of the letter—the *name* of the letter—starts the word:

A ble seamen should know how to swim.
B tray no secrets.
C for yourself.
D ny it not!
E Z does it!
F ort properly applied moves mountains. (Effort)
G whiz!
H erished fancy may lead to disappointment. (A cherished)
I dleness is tempting.
J walkers increase the dangers of driving.
K nes are carried for style or for support. (Canes)
L ephants will leave a bale of hay for a pint of peanuts.
M ty cans make the most noise.
N ter the station through, not under, the stile.
O say can you ski?
P nuts for you!
Q for the bus; don't crowd.
R tillery is growing obsolete.
S ential information should not be withheld.
T dious T sing T ches naught. T hee!
U are the one for me.
V hicles are not allowed on the sidewalk.
X terminate the termites. X ellent!
Y se guy, eh?
Z ro is the final score.

Give the group paper and pencil, explain Phony Alphabet, read aloud the sentences for A and B, and thus enAble them to B gin their own.

Two oral alphabet games are often played. The first is "I love my love . . ." This goes through a fixed ritual of sentences, all of which the first player completes with words that start with A. The next player repeats the sentences with B words. Round and round till the alphabet is complete, with poor lovers (those that cannot supply all the words with the appropriate letter) dropping out. The sentences are: I love my love with an (A) because he (she, if a man is speaking) is _____. I hate him because he is _____. I feed him with _____ and _____. His name is _____ and he lives in _____. He took me to _____ and treated me to _____ and _____. We were married in _____ and now I am _____.

This was a popular game during the Restoration, after Charles II of England in 1660 brought back frivolity from France. And it remained popular. In 1872, Alice slipped into the game, while advancing on the other side of the Looking-Glass:

> "I love my love with an H," Alice couldn't help beginning, "because he is Happy. I hate him with an H because he is Hideous. I feed him with—Ham-sandwiches and Hay. His name is Haigha, and he lives—"
>
> "He lives on the hill," the King remarked simply, without the least idea that he was joining in the game.

The other oral game takes a repetitive trip. "I'm going on a journey and I'm taking . . ." The first player takes anything (either appropriate or amusing) that begins with A. The second player repeats all the first has said, then adds the item beginning with B that he will take. Each repeats all that those before have said, continuing until all but one have slipped in the repetition and dropped out.

By the time you get through these, you should know the alphabet backwards. Indeed, can you recite the alphabet backwards? Backwards, omitting the five vowels?

With a group, try the alphabet backwards, each to give the proper letter instantly. There'll probably be more than one stumble.

Lipograms

The opposite of a pangram is a Lipogram. Lipography is writing that avoids the use of a particular letter. It was a playful practice in ancient times. In the Dark Ages a Greek writer, Tryphiodorus, tried to lighten the times with a new version of Homer's *Odyssey*. From each of its twenty-four books he omitted one of the twenty-four letters of the Greek alphabet: no *alpha* in Book One, no *beta* in Book Two, and so on from *alpha* to *omega*, soup to nuts. Try writing just one fairly long sentence without using the letter *e*, and you'll have a slight idea of the trouble he must have had.

There was a petty Persian poetaster who went to the great poet Jami, hoping to be praised because he'd written a poem without the letter *alif.* Jami read it attentively, thought a moment, then said: "It would be better if you left out the other letters too."

Nevertheless, on a lawn outside a church in merry England, there is a neat lipogrammatic sign. It reads, in large letters: "CH_ _CH." Underneath is the question "What is missing?" and in a corner is the answer: "U R." Could you refuse such an invitation to attend next Sunday?

Speaking of English churches, more than one carries, under the tablet of the Ten Commandments, these mysterious letters:

PRSVR Y PRFCT MN
VR KP THS PRCPTS TN (45)

Here are some more or less well-known old sayings, with a dash for every vowel. See whether you can complete them.

1. Th_ b_ _ghs th_t b_ _r m_st h_ng l_w_st.
2. Th_ h_gh_r _n _p_ g_ _s, th_ m_r_ h_ sh_ws h_s t_ _l.
3. H_p_ _s _s _n_xp_ns_v_ _s d_sp_ _r.
4. _cc_r_c_ _s _ d_t_, n_t _ v_rt_ _.
5. Th_ wh_ _l th_t d_ _s th_ sq_ _ _k_ng g_ts th_ gr_ _s_.
6. Th_ l_z_ d_g l_ _n_d _g_ _nst th_ w_ll t_ b_rk.

Here are some words with the vowels left out. The number of vowels is given, with a clue.

7. H (3) a state of the Union
8. W (3) another state
9. HLTH (2) a different state
10. - (2) an extinct bird; its plumage made robes for Hawaiian kings
11. HW (4) a new state
12. NN (3) a vegetable that grows underground
13. KLL (4) a musical instrument (from 11)
14. RP (4) a continent
15. FR (3) a magical creature, usually carries a wand
16. JN (2) unite

17. R (3) an open space
18. RL (4) it helps your TV set (46)

The Longer the Shorter

What is the longest word in the language? Some of the candi-
dates are not really words at all. Shakespeare was playful when
he coined the twenty-seven-letter word *honorificabilitudinitatibus,* alternating consonants and vowels. But this must
take a back seat behind the thirty-four letters of *supercali-
fragilisticexpialidocious,* which rhymes with *precocious* and
atrocious in a song in the motion picture *Mary Poppins.*

If you really want to find long manufactured words, you can
go hunting in the book *Funnymans Fake*—excuse me, *Finnegans Wake*—by the irrepressible Joyce. He has put in ten
"thunderwords," each of which contains one hundred letters.
These may have longitude, but they leave their interpreters
considerable latitude.

Perhaps the longest word actually used—well, not in everyday speech, but in meaningful discourse—is the term describing
a church attitude: *antidisestablishmentarianism.* Its twenty-
eight letters, however, were recently increased, in a letter to the
London *Times* speaking of a man who merely pretended to
have such an attitude, and who therefore argued *quasiantidises-
tablishmentarianistically,* achieving a total of forty letters. You
can't get much longer than that, unless you resort to Welsh or
American Indian place names, or to the names of some of the
more complex chemical compounds. The full chemical name of
the tryptophan synthetase A protein has 1,913 letters!

All such rigmarole aside, everyone knows that the longest
word in the English language is *smiles:* between its first and last
letter, there's a *mile.*

How careful are you? Do you believe everything you see in
print? Nobody told me the "full alphabet" in the Bible (Ezra
7:21) was missing a *j;* I looked for the passage and counted. And
if you have counted the letters in the word above from the
London *Times,* you've discovered that there are not forty letters but only thirty-nine. Don't accept blindly; check!

The longest English word of one syllable seems to be *strengths,* which has nine letters. Oddly enough, there's a word one letter shorter that has five syllables: *ideality.* Some words —*latchstring, catchphrase, eschscholtzia*—have six consonants in succession. When a bookkeeper has an assistant, this sub-bookkeeper has to struggle along with four doubled letters in a row. And there is one word that becomes shorter when you make it longer. Let's call it *short.*

5

THE MARCH OF MEANING:
CATEGORIES, COLORS, CLICHÉS,
CRYPTOGRAMS, CATCHES

Nobody knows how words first came to have meanings attached to them. A long time before history starts, the grunts and squeals and cries of primitive men began to become attached to certain feelings or objects, until the sound came to "mean" the thing to which it was attached.

Since the main purpose of language is to communicate, there must be rather general agreement as to what our words mean. Very often you can judge the sense of a new word from the way it's used, helped out by all the words around. But is it yours to command? Can you recognize it when you see it by itself? That is, can you pull it out of your mind to make use of it, just the word you want? Let's try.

Pick

In each of the following lists, select the word closest in meaning to the first word. Try only ten at a time.

A
1. appreciate—(a) price; (b) recognize value; (c) diminish; (d) climb the peak.
2. apprehensive—(a) horrible; (b) catching on; (c) fearful; (d) clinging.
3. approximate—(a) come near; (b) tell the time; (c) guess; (d) deny.

4. composure—(a) inventing; (b) calmness; (c) putting together; (d) effrontery.
5. salvage—(a) smooth over; (b) wreckage; (c) save; (d) chew upon.
6. aperture—(a) freshness; (b) opening; (c) disclosure; (d) discrimination.
7. raiment—(a) clothing; (b) dryness; (c) downpour; (d) shine.
8. enervate—(a) nervous; (b) give vigor to; (c) energetic; (d) weaken.
9. copious—(a) repeating; (b) mimicking; (c) flowing; (d) abundant.
10. bewilder—(a) concoct; (b) contort; (c) anger; (d) confuse.

B

1. controversy—(a) dispute; (b) angle; (c) opposition; (d) treasure.
2. rancor—(a) resentment; (b) position; (c) depth; (d) support.
3. glut—(a) pour; (b) hunger; (c) stick; (d) satiate.
4. furtive—(a) thievish; (b) stealthy; (c) heavy; (d) warm.
5. pollute—(a) consecrate; (b) vote; (c) contaminate; (d) defy.
6. civility—(a) citizenship; (b) politeness; (c) right to vote; (d) rudeness.
7. jerkin—(a) twisting; (b) dried meat; (c) jacket; (d) roast beef.
8. brimstone—(a) gravel; (b) large rock; (c) pebbles; (d) sulfur.
9. celestial—(a) harmonious; (b) vegetable; (c) heavenly; (d) speedy.
10. confidential—(a) private; (b) deposited; (c) cheating; (d) scored.

C

1. expiate—(a) pay back; (b) empty; (c) atone for; (d) hurry.
2. redundant—(a) superfluous; (b) necessary; (c) flowing; (d) thundering.
3. ordain—(a) suppose; (b) decree; (c) scorn; (d) hate.
4. legacy—(a) travel plan; (b) bequest; (c) distance; (d) ability.
5. hazard—(a) a bird; (b) game; (c) challenge; (d) risk.
6. guise—(a) flattery; (b) appearance; (c) persons; (d) talk.
7. doleful—(a) poor; (b) promising; (c) sorrowful; (d) helpful.
8. shackle—(a) fetter; (b) upset; (c) house; (d) scramble.
9. mediocre—(a) card game; (b) unhappy; (c) commonplace; (d) countryside.
10. inimical—(a) hostile; (b) copying; (c) unlike; (d) overcoming.

D

1. murky—(a) disdainful; (b) fat; (c) gloomy; (d) madly.
2. retract—(a) trace; (b) hasten; (c) reform; (d) withdraw.
3. histrionic—(a) actual; (b) theatrical; (c) important; (d) rioting.
4. felon—(a) criminal; (b) tumbler; (c) smart; (d) unhappy.
5. literally—(a) exactly; (b) excellently; (c) stylishly; (d) untidily.
6. squander—(a) splash; (b) roam; (c) waste; (d) idle.
7. brusque—(a) clean; (b) dusty; (c) speedy; (d) abrupt.
8. broach—(a) jewel; (b) lock; (c) open; (d) discuss.
9. spurious—(a) inquisitive; (b) false; (c) hastening; (d) angry.
10. languor—(a) distaste; (b) noise; (c) distance; (d) listlessness.

E

1. subtle—(a) underground; (b) unfortunate; (c) crass; (d) crafty.
2. typify—(a) print; (b) exemplify; (c) stupefy; (d) condemn.
3. burnish—(a) supply; (b) endeavor; (c) brighten; (d) smudge.
4. levity—(a) flightiness; (b) weight; (c) pressure; (d) exemption.
5. embellish—(a) adorn; (b) threaten; (c) spoil; (d) abash.
6. vacillate—(a) subordinate; (b) turn; (c) slow down; (d) waver.
7. accede—(a) take over; (b) follow; (c) consent; (d) repeat.
8. harbinger—(a) collector; (b) forerunner; (c) supporter; (d) follower.
9. solace—(a) comfort; (b) only one; (c) tie; (d) triumph.
10. affable—(a) horrid; (b) comic; (c) sociable; (d) considerable. (47)

Match

Here is another game for testing your knowledge of meanings. Try it on your friends. Dictate two columns, the first numbered one to ten, the second lettered *a* to *j*. Each is then to write next to the numbered word the letter of the word nearest to it in meaning. Here are two sets for you to match:

A
1. fragile		a. leave
2. evoke		b. impatient
3. mortify		c. unconcealed
4. relinquish		d. summon
5. candor		e. trim
6. restive		f. swallow up
7. prune		g. rebounding
8. overt		h. breakable
9. absorb		i. frankness
10. resilient		j. shame

B
1. tyro		a. loathe
2. pertinent		b. ability
3. malign		c. merry
4. abhor		d. kindle
5. jovial		e. beginner
6. assail		f. threat
7. faculty		g. slander
8. menace		h. nearness
9. ignite		i. applicable
10. proximity		j. attack (48)

Here is a double match. Select the pair of words that fits the sentence:

1. An _____ is a thing not to be _____.
   (a) increment . . . concluded; (b) excuse . . . denied; (c) opportunity . . . overlooked; (d) apology . . . tendered.
2. He _____ not to _____ the proposal.
   (a) endeavored . . . recognize; (b) decided . . . accept; (c) managed . . . undermine; (d) undertook . . . mismanage.
3. A _____ is a delaying action in a _____.
   (a) strike . . . factory; (b) curb . . . business deal; (c) filibuster . . . legislature; (d) handicap . . . contest.

4. To _____ is to get back one's _____.
   (a) restore . . . possessions; (b) remedy . . . afflictions; (c) reclaim
   . . . rights; (d) recuperate . . . health. (49)

Here is still another kind of match, a ratio. In mathematics, you write a ratio like this: 2:4::4:8. You read it: "Two is to four as four is to eight." This means that the relationship between two and four is the same as that between four and eight. We can also write 2:4::720:1440. Why? Here are some relationships in meaning. Select the right word to fill the blank.

1. Calm is to agitated as high is to _____.
   (a) towering; (b) tall; (c) low; (d) stirring.
2. Snore is to sleep as _____ is to cold.
   (a) winter; (b) sniffle; (c) muffler; (d) snow.
3. Gill is to fish as _____ is to man.
   (a) arm; (b) nostril; (c) breathing; (d) fin.
4. Quick is to speedy as summary is to _____.
   (a) story; (b) synopsis; (c) lively; (d) detail.
5. Beatles are to music as Bogart is to _____.
   (a) beards; (b) films; (c) fame; (d) audiences. (50)

Intruder

Another way to look at meanings is by way of associated words. In each of the twelve groups below, one word does not belong. Write it and the reason it is an intruder.

1. twenty-two	six	nine	fourteen
2. sleet	snow	hail	frost
3. potato	cabbage	onion	carrot
4. remainder	increment	leavings	remnant
5. cone	triangle	pyramid	sphere
6. marbles	dice	tennis balls	soccer balls
7. pentagon	quadrilateral	square	ellipse
8. raccoon	squirrel	woodcock	chipmunk
9. inscrutable	feasable	peaceable	workable
10. fragrance	tint	aroma	perfume
11. Minnesota	Minneapolis	Arkansas	Ohio
12. run	gallop	meander	hasten (51)

You can readily make more of these to try on your friends.

Sometimes you can tell, from one part of a word, in what range of meaning it belongs. Words ending in -mancy, for example, usually deal with magic, especially with foretelling or preshaping the future. See how many *-mancy* words you can write down in three minutes, with their special meanings. *Necromancy,* for instance, is black magic, involving use of the powers of the dead. *Pyromancy* means reading the future in the flickering of flames; it is not a contributing cause to pyromania. (There are many manias and phobias, too!)

Do the same with the *-ology* words. This should be easy, as there must be over a hundred of them, from *anthropology* to *zoology.* With a very few exceptions, like *anthology* and *apology,* these words refer to the study of a particular field. Do you know what *bryology* means? Or *osteology? Penology* is not the study of penmanship. *Phrenology* is no longer considered a serious study. *Taxology* has nothing to do with your income, and *nosology* has nothing to do with your smell.

There are, of course, many more words in the language than you will ever have occasion to use. I myself have compiled a dictionary of forgotten words. Just for a flavoring, here are two words you can use that may give an amusing turn to your conversation. After you've made a statement, you may calmly declare: "And that's apodeictic!" You may send your listeners to the dictionary, to discover that you've merely stated: "That's a fact." When someone else makes a statement, you may say, in an approving tone: "That's phthiriatic!" Since the *ph* is silent (thigh-ree-att'-ic), a dictionary hunt will probably be fruitless, and at your leisure you can reveal that you've said: "That's lousy!"

Categories

Categories has been played for centuries. Young men and girls used to play it standing in a circle on the village green, one in the center with a ball. He'd toss the ball to one in the circle and at the same time name one of the three kingdoms, animal, vegetable, or mineral. The player had to catch the ball and at the same time name something in that category: for instance, *jackass, spinach,* or *mercury,* according to which kingdom was called. Later on—or when it rained—the game was played indoors, pointing instead of tossing a ball. Another game with the three kingdoms is in Chapter 13.

Categories can also be played as a written game. You make a series of boxes, and down one side, write a short word or name. On top, write a few categories, such as *jewels, titles* (of books, songs, films), *vegetables,* etc. Then the columns must be filled with words belonging to the category on top, and beginning with the letter on the left. Here is one filled in:

	Countries	Famous Persons	Animals
A	Afghanistan	King Alfred	anaconda
L	Liberia	Lochinvar	leopard
I	Iceland	Isaiah	ichthyosaurus
C	Canada	Cleopatra	cougar
E	Ecuador	Emerson	elephant

Linking of ideas forms another game: Association. This is started by a leader, who gives the first word. After that he gives no word but keeps check. At once the next player says a word suggested by, or somehow related to, the first. Next player at once gives a word suggested by the second. And so on, everyone giving his word within five seconds. After a dozen words or so, the leader suddenly cries: "Reverse!" At once, the next player gives the word just spoken; the next, the word before that, and so on, down to the word the game started with. Anyone taking more than five seconds or (on the reverse trip) giving the wrong word has one point scored against him. (Leader keeps score without interrupting.)

Repeat the process for a few rounds, with the leader giving a new first word each time. At the end, the player with the fewest points against him wins. A chain might run like this: black—panther—wild—tame—elephant—circus—peanuts—cartoon—music—rock—hard—soft—cheese. Reverse!

A more leisurely linking that works well with from two to six players is to build a complete story. The first player makes up a situation, with a couple of characters. After three or four sentences, he says: "And then——" and stops. The next player at once continues the story, going along until he says: "And then——" Next player now has his turn. They continue, perhaps going around twice or more, until the story comes to an end.

The object is to carry the characters along, with surprise twists and amusing shiftings from what has gone before. When the story ends, there is often a lively discussion as each player tells what he had in mind to follow his section of the tale.

Colors

No sooner did words have meanings than meanings began to spread, often by association. After the head on your body, men spoke of the head of the family, the head of the tribe. Later, they looked at a heading, or they tried to forge ahead. A foot became a measure; so did a hand (four inches), still used for the height of horses. In England you stand on scales to be weighed by the stone (fourteen pounds). These extensions of meaning the Elizabethan called colors; we call them figures of speech. A figure of speech is the use of a word in a new way, expanding its meaning, adding a touch of surprise, of freshness, of beauty.

Probably many of the words we now use in ordinary conversation were once fresh figures of speech. But through the centuries, the new meaning became the usual one, ordinary and perhaps dull. The shine of its early days grew dim. So writers and speakers continue to seek fresh ways of referring to familiar things. Look at the words newspaper sportswriters use, and see how they strain for new figures of speech.

Often, without knowing it, they return to old pastures. (That's a figure of speech too; you didn't picture the writer rushing to a meadow to feed his fancy!) Look at the word *pluck*. A plucky fellow: we all know what that means. But a hundred and fifty years ago it didn't have that meaning. Then, *the pluck* was the term farmers used for the viscera, the part of a fowl they would put their hand in and pluck out. Now that first meaning is almost forgotten, and *pluck* is the usual term for courage and endurance. So now people want a fresher word. Where do they find it? They go right back to the viscera and exclaim: "That guy's got guts!"

That is the way slang gets started.

Everybody wants to use fresh, colorful language. There are two general ways of making your words more lively.

First, instead of using a word that gathers in a whole class, like *man* or *person,* you can select a more specific, more precise term, such as *gentleman, mountebank, lawyer, lout.*

Colorfill

In each sentence, substitute for the word in italics a more precise and colorful word from the list given. For a group, dictate the sentences and the words. After all have chosen, each must be ready to justify his choice. No one of the substitute words is necessarily the best, and some may not fit at all.

1. He looked across the *dry* plain, and wondered how anyone could live there.
   sear, parched, arid, scorched, withered.
2. As the bird flew, its *red* wings made a bright streak amid the leaves.
   crimson, scarlet, ruby, cardinal, maroon, vermilion.
3. The two men sat down to *talk* about the issues.
   converse, chat, discuss (omit *about*)*, prattle, prate.*
4. As they approached the botanical gardens, the *smell* grew stronger.
   aroma, scent, perfume, fragrance, incense, stench, reek.
5. There was *small* reason to believe that the *small* fellow would win.
   slight, diminutive, tiny, little, minute, microscopic, slender, frail, flimsy, meager.
6. The *tall* stranger stood in front of the *tall* building watching the sunset.
   high, gigantic, lanky, ranging, towering, lengthy, skyscraping, cloud-touching.

The second way to make your words more lively is, instead of using a word to mean just what it says, to use it figuratively. If you call a man a beanpole or say he's as tall as a lamppost, everyone will understand what you mean. If you say that he bit off more than he can chew, your listeners will not think of him with a mouthful of beefsteak. They'll know you mean he's tried something beyond his powers.

Clichés

Figures of speech are common in all languages, from the slang of the week to the poems of the centuries. The trouble is that once you hear them, you say them; they are so apt that everybody says them, and soon the color and freshness have been worn away. A person you like is *cool*; a person you don't like is *square*. You tend to blame things on *the Establishment*. By the time this is printed, these expressions may be *old hat*, and new terms may be on every tongue.

Some expressions have been used so often that they have become hackneyed—a *hackney* was a horse anyone could hire. These tired terms are also called clichés. They used to be colorful and still may be a quick and emphatic way of saying what you have in mind. But usually they seem faded and out of date, and we ought to find fresher ways of conveying our ideas and our feelings.

Select five of the common expressions below, and use each one in a sentence. Players read their sentences; the group decides which are most effective.

Then rewrite your sentences, with another expression replacing the cliché. Again, the group decides which are most successful. Here is a batch of clichés:

there's the rub	foregone conclusion
a tower of strength	castles in the air
the supreme sacrifice	a pretty kettle of fish
but it was not to be	split hairs
(one's) tender mercies	hit the ceiling
bonds of matrimony	move heaven and earth
make a virtue of necessity	by the skin of (one's) teeth
neither rhyme nor reason	take (one) down a peg
method in his madness	speed the parting guest

his own worst enemy	leave no stone unturned
the fair sex	through thick and thin
blessing in disguise	a lump in (one's) throat
the finger of fate	single blessedness
the acid test	(one's) better half
an aching void	

Smile at a Simile

Some comparisons have become so familiar that the first part almost automatically clicks the rest into your mind. This, too, makes a game. The leader says the first part; a player completes the expression. If he can't, he drops out, and the next player tries. (If nobody can give the ending, no one drops out.) Continue until all the expressions—or all the players—are used up. As:

1. black as	21. snug as	41. fit as	61. clear as
2. red as	22. innocent as	42. flat as	62. slippery as
3. dumb as	23. fresh as	43. blind as	63. sharp as
4. mute as	24. pert as	44. light as	64. bright as
5. plump as	25. tall as	45. hot as	65. smart as
6. quick as	26. high as	46. cold as	66. clean as
7. thin as	27. long as	47. cool as	67. bald as
8. skinny as	28. large as	48. fat as	68. pleased as
9. quiet as	29. mad as	49. poor as	69. busy as
10. ugly as	30. spry as	50. rich as	70. drunk as
11. pretty as	31. free as	51. patient as	71. neat as
12. pale as	32. plenty as	52. stubborn as	72. ragged as
13. white as	33. easy as	53. proud as	73. sound as
14. sweet as	34. dry as	54. dead as	74. alike as
15. sour as	35. brown as	55. cross as	75. sure as
16. deaf as	36. naked as	56. angry as	76. welcome as
17. merry as	37. brave as	57. dull as	77. thick as
18. gay as	38. good as	58. plain as	78. useless as
19. smooth as	39. tight as	59. hard as	79. crowded as
20. much sense as	40. right as	60. soft as	80. old as (52)

Shakespeare in *Hamlet* says "deep as a well . . . wide as a church door." The motto (1970) of the rock group Sly and the Family Stone is "sly as a fox and cold as a stone." I hope that while you're trying these games, you're not as slow as molasses in January.

Catches

Meanings are sometimes difficult to discern or are deliberately entangled in double-talk. Thus, if a woman hears a man remark: "A woman will lie as fast as a dog will lick a dish," she may at once riposte: "Men never lie but when the holly is green." After a moment, you wake to recognize that holly is an evergreen.

Words and messages with two meanings, one on the surface, one somehow hidden, have been used in more than play. The great French cardinal, Richelieu, once gave a man a letter to the French ambassador at Rome. Read right across the page, it was a high recommendation. But after the influential man who had asked for it had read it, Richelieu folded the paper in half to seal it. When read down the half-page, the letter warned the ambassador that the man was a scoundrel.

Some verses, if you read them just as they are written, form a blessing, but if you read alternate lines, they utter a curse. The essayist Joseph Addison called these "witches' prayers."

Such a two-tongued term is called a *double entendre.* Thus the poet Heine wrote to a scribbler who had sent him his latest work: "Thank you for your book. I shall lose no time reading it." Sheridan said, to a bore who was fishing for an invitation: "If you come within ten miles of my country house, I beg you will stop there for the night."

The usual churchly greeting, "Peace be with you," in Latin is *Pax tecum.* Jonathan Swift ended a letter: "As to your enemies, pox take 'em!" The same pronunciation, but *pox* is a disease.

The smart young man remarked to his rival: "The more I think of you, the less I think of you."

An equivoque or double entendre just pretends to hide its meaning; it wants the insinuation to show through.

Cryptograms

Many persons, however, seek really private means of communication, to be understood only by themselves and one or two intimates. On a small scale, these are called ciphers. Samuel Pepys wrote much of his noted diary in a cipher that was not deciphered for many years. Ciphers have been devised within the Shakespearean plays to prove that they were written by Bacon. I do not know who eggs them on.

A simple cipher indicates that Shakespeare worked secretly on the King James Bible. In Psalm 46, the forty-sixth word is *shake;* the forty-sixth word from the end is *spear.* Why forty-six? Because in 1610, when the King James translation was completed, Shakespeare was forty-six years old. Note also that Shakespeare was born on April 23 and died on April 23; 23 + 23 = 46. The twenty-third Psalm, which Shakespeare evidently translated, is the best known of the Bible psalms.

More seriously, the Cryptogram (the word means hidden or secret writing) has been used for thousands of years to exchange messages with legates, ambassadors, and generals at the front. Nowadays, the codes are put through computers, and it is increasingly difficult to devise codes the enemy cannot break.

For play among friends, you can use two simpler codes. The first is simple enough for a passage to be given to someone to decipher. The second is practically undecipherable.

1. Write down the message you want to send. Then rewrite it, changing every letter to the one three beyond it in the alphabet (or five beyond, or any number agreed upon with the person who is to receive it). Leave a space after every five letters, whether a word ends there or not. You can make messages in this fashion and give them to friends who do not know the code. Let them take a message home, decipher it, and send you an answer in the same code.

2. Agree with your friend on a book you both will have and use. The day of the month on the top of your letter shows the page you are using. Write your message, with the date on top. Then hunt on the proper page for each letter in your words. Keep them in the correct order, but use two letters: the first letter shows the line; the second, the number on the line. Thus *cf* means: line three, the sixth letter. Leave a space after every tenth letter you put down—five pairs. Never use the same line for the same letter; if *cf* is the first letter *e* of the real message,

the next *e* should be *gn* or the like. Then you may defy anyone to break the code.

Relations

Many a problem arises over the relations between words or between ideas. Some special problems arise over human relations. See what you can do with a few.

1. Arthur's daughter Ada married Ben. Arthur married Beth, Ben's daughter by a previous marriage. Arthur and Beth have a son, Simon. What relation is Ada to Simon?

2. Sisters and brothers have I none,
   But that man's father is my father's son.
Who is "that man"?

3. The doctor said: "You have the same problem as my brother Henry." The patient knew Henry had no brother. Was the doctor lying?

4. The most widely known question not about a relation but of this puzzling sort is: How old is Anne? It's proof of the fact that something may be simple, yet far from plain. Every word in the following statement, except a name, a number, and a plural, is a familiar one-syllable word; yet it has puzzled many in many generations:

Mary is twice as old as Anne was when Mary was half as old as Anne will be when she (Anne) is three times as old as Mary was when Mary was three times as old as Anne. The sum of their ages is thirty-two. How old is Anne?

5. Take a plain card. On one side of it write: "The sentence on the other side is true." On the other side of it write: "The sentence on the other side is false." Set your friends to work disentangling these statements.

6. A says B lies. B says C lies. C says A and B lie. Which one is telling the truth?

7. Saint Paul (Epistle to Titus, 1:12–13) got into one of these mix-ups. He declared that the Cretan who said all Cretans always lie was a true witness.

8. Ask a friend to promise to answer two questions truthfully, *the second first,* after he hears them both:

> Question 1. Will you have dinner with me tonight?
> Question 2. Will your answer to the first question be the same as your answer to this?

9. Let's go back to Saint Paul's Cretans, but let's be a little more generous. Say only half always lie, the other half always tell the truth. A stranger who knows this comes to a fork in the road. A smiling townsman stands there. What one question can the stranger ask, to be answered yes or no, that will ensure his getting the right direction to the town, whether the Cretan is a liar or a truther?

Then suppose that, instead of a fork, there are several cross-roads. What one question will ensure the stranger's finding the right direction?

10. John Doe, a lawyer, gave Richard Roe free use of his office facilities, on Richard's agreement to pay John as soon as he won his first case. Richard was admitted to the bar, but he had no clients. After six months, John grew impatient and sued him. John figured he had a sure case: If I win, the court will order him to pay; if I lose, he must pay according to the terms of the agreement. How did Richard see the suit? (53)

There are books devoted to problems of this kind, verbal or logical. We hope these are all clear. Now let's clear out of this chapter.

6

SYNONYMS, ANTONYMS, WORDS THAT CONTRADICT THEMSELVES, DOUBLE WORDS, IRREVERSIBLES, SHIFTIES, AND EUPHEMY

Through the wisdom, imagination, and plumb Dutch luck of our great-grandfathers, the English language gives us a choice of many words. Often, alas, we are too lazy, if not too ignorant, to choose.

We may, for instance, see a man approaching us along the street, and exclaim: "How big he is!" But we have not in the least made clear how big—or big how? Is he tall, towering, even gigantic, but maybe lean, lanky, long-legged? Is he hulky, massive, heavy? Is he brawny, strapping, beefy, or perhaps bloated, blowsy? Or is he stocky but fleshy, thickset, stout, fat, obese, paunchy, portly, potbellied if not bellicose? There is a character in Rabelais' *Gargantua* who trundles his belly before him on a wheelbarrow. (Perhaps you know somebody who could use one.)

Humpty Dumpty, when Alice is through the Looking-Glass, tells her that he pays his words to work for him. On this side of the mirror, the work may be yours, but the words are free. You don't have to pay your penny when "you takes your choice."

Many words are terms in a polarity. That is, there may be a word at either end of a scale, like the North Pole and the

South Pole, with perhaps another term midway, like the Equator. Love—indifference—hate. But where those dashes are
there may be in-between words: *fondness, affection, liking, incli-
nation, fancy* on the one side; on the other *dislike, aversion,
antipathy, abhorrence, loathing, detestation.* Indeed, if we call
hate zero on the scale, these last three words may be below zero.

You can see the play of early slang in the word *fondness.* It
first meant *foolishness.* Something of that meaning lingers in Sir
John Suckling's seventeenth-century verse:

> Why so pale and wan, fond lover?
> Prithee, why so pale?
> Will, when looking well can't move her,
> Looking ill prevail?
> Prithee, why so pale?

And nowadays, when *fond* has lost that meaning, you hear
people pick up the same image and say, "He's crazy about her,"
or, "He's mad about her"—not *at* her—or even "She's nuts
about him." Lovers are little changed. And on the whole words
haven't changed very much, either. It's fun to know their history. For a glimpse of that, wait for Chapter 8.

Words that have meanings nearly alike, that are on the same
half of the polarity, are called synonyms. A good check of your
skill in handling words is your ability to distinguish among
synonyms, to select just the one to convey the precise shade of
your meaning.

Synonyms

Play this game with two to six players. Select one group of
synonyms all players are to use. Every player writes a sentence
for each of three words in that group, trying to make clear the
exact sense of the chosen word. Players read their sentences in
turn, and must be ready to defend their choice. The players
decide which sentences are most effective. You may choose
from the words for *big* above, or the love-hate batch, or one of
the eight clusters below. Or you may make a group of your own.

1. brave, courageous, plucky, fearless, foolhardy, reckless, bold, daring, valiant, gallant, undaunted.
2. near, close, adjacent, adjoining, contiguous, neighboring, next to.
3. conceal, hide, secrete, seclude, veil, suppress.
4. despise, disdain, scorn, spurn, hold in contempt.
5. forgive, pardon, absolve, condone, excuse, exonerate, acquit.
6. quarrel, struggle, dispute, debate, battle, fight, combat, contest, tussle, match, bout.
7. dominion, rule, sway, mastery, power.
8. spicy, seasoned, pungent, hot, peppery, piquant, sharp.

Sometimes there are pairs of words that invite confusion. You are not likely to mistake the word *plumb*, in the first sentence of this chapter, for the fruit called *plum*, but you may not know that the *plum* in *plum pudding* is not "the fruit with flattish stone and sweet flesh" at all but a raisin! Can you tell how the words *shameful, shameless*, and *ashamed* are to be used?

For these, or any pair of the following words, play as with a group of synonyms. Be ready to justify your sentences by explaining the words you've used.

1. uninterested—disinterested; 2. precipitate—precipitous; 3. persuade—convince (even the proper *New York Times* has used these improperly); 4. virtually—virtuously; 5. fatal—fateful; 6. repulsion—revulsion; 7. inflammable—inflammatory; 8. confident—confidential; 9. laudable—laudatory; 10. delighted—delightful; 11. regretful—regrettable; 12. precedents—precedence; 13. condemn—contemn; 14. Hibernian—hibernating; 15. semantic—Semitic; 16. currant—current; 17. liquor—liquid.

If you're thinking of becoming a doctor, be sure you can tell a podiatrist from a pediatrician, and a pathfinder from a pathologist. Sometimes the confusion has gone so far that words are hopelessly entangled, and their usefulness is largely lost. I looked up *piteous* in the dictionary and found it defined as *pitiful;* I looked up *pitiful,* and found that it is defined as *pitiable.* As Shakespeare puts it, pity 'tis, 'tis true!

Antonyms

Just as there are words alike in meaning, so at the ends of the poles the opposites reside: *love* and *hate; harmony* and *discord.* These are called antonyms.

The game of Opposites can be played at almost any age. A five-year-old has delightedly responded "top" to my "bottom," "up" to my "down," "back" to my "front," and so on.

You can play the game at another level. First player gives a word—for example, *bravery*—and points. The player pointed at, within ten seconds, gives a sentence containing an antonym of the given word: "He showed his cowardice by running away from the battlefield." The player that answered then gives a word and points. And so on. Deduct one point for not having a ready sentence or for an incorrect one. When you stop, the player with fewest points against him wins.

A word may have more than one nearly opposite term. For instance, *noise* may be countered by *silence, quiet, stillness.* If the pointer objects to a word, the group decides whether it is appropriate.

Sometimes, in fact, a word may have antonyms on more than one level of meaning. You may argue that *noise* means *disorganized, disagreeable sound,* so that its opposite, from this point of view, can be *harmony. Fragrant* may have as an antonym *stinking* but also *odorless.* Such a second antonym is usually the middle term of the polarity.

Almost any word can be suggested for this game. Here are a few to get you started:

> modesty (vanity); mystify (enlighten); loquacious (taciturn); belief (incredulity); cleanse (dirty, befoul); lenient (severe); occasional (habitual); dynamic (static); caution (rashness); indifference (concern); fickle (constant); interrupted (continuous); superfluous (insufficient); placate (enrage); greedy (generous); miser (spendthrift); ruthless (merciful); feeble (powerful); persevere (abandon, give up); reluctant (eager); heedless (attentive); conform (differ, rebel).

In the following sets of words pick the word that is an antonym of the first word. Try only ten at a time.

A
1. relax—(a) spin; (b) rush; (c) tighten; (d) rest
2. complete—(a) final; (b) fulfill; (c) partial; (d) struggle.
3. sufficient—(a) hopeful; (b) inadequate; (c) ranging; (d) effective.
4. secede—(a) come around; (b) retreat; (c) recede; (d) join.
5. precipice—(a) episode; (b) plain; (c) hasty; (d) dawdling.
6. impromptu—(a) hurried; (b) fashionable; (c) harmonious; (d) planned.
7. immaculate—(a) unclean; (b) spotless; (c) decorated; (d) enclosed.
8. pulchritude—(a) fancy; (b) hideousness; (c) garlanded; (d) weariness.
9. rigid—(a) pliable; (b) firm; (c) rational; (d) borderless.
10. flattery—(a) ointment; (b) tegument; (c) frankness; (d) incense.

B
1. scarcity—(a) absence; (b) plenty; (c) trial; (d) hopefulness.
2. famous—(a) unknown; (b) unconcerned; (c) happy; (d) dismal.
3. impotence—(a) power; (b) strategy; (c) weakness; (d) denial.
4. vanish—(a) display; (b) transfer; (c) appear; (d) account for.
5. dexterity—(a) vanity; (b) clumsiness; (c) propriety; (d) evacuation.
6. exonerate—(a) accuse; (b) defend; (c) convict; (d) persecute.
7. renovate—(a) balance; (b) collect; (c) fasten; (d) ruin.
8. portray—(a) resemble; (b) counteract; (c) look; (d) distort.
9. fragile—(a) tough; (b) frail; (c) tempting; (d) passionate.
10. skeptical—(a) unconcerned; (b) trusting; (c) merry; (d) in the dumps.

C
1. declivity—(a) consent; (b) ascent; (c) assent; (d) conflict.
2. reject—(a) select; (b) destroy; (c) measure; (d) dispose of.
3. penalize—(a) draw; (b) happen; (c) destroy; (d) reward.
4. drab—(a) happy; (b) entertained; (c) colorful; (d) enticing.
5. occupied—(a) furnished; (b) extinct; (c) wasteful; (d) idle.
6. expose—(a) conceal; (b) detract; (c) fancy; (d) retract.
7. rejoice—(a) enjoy; (b) grieve; (c) welcome; (d) return.
8. despair—(a) confine; (b) release; (c) hope; (d) fashion.
9. disparage—(a) praise; (b) restore; (c) confirm; (d) confuse.
10. damage—(a) return; (b) repair; (c) relate; (d) recognize. (54)

Ante Up!

We usually measure opposition to something by calling for pros and cons. (This must not be taken as a sign that *Con*gress is opposed to *progress*.) *Anti-* as well as *con-* means *against*. *Anti-* may confuse you, however, because the *i* drops out before a vowel, as in *antagonist,* and who can say that the prefix was not *ante-,* which means *before?*

So let's see what you can do with *anti-*. Write the words beginning with *ant* that fit the clues below. (Some of the *ants* have nothing to do with the prefix *anti-*.)

1. make hostile
2. way down south
3. animal that thrives on insects
4. place where you are kept waiting
5. before Noah sailed in his ark
6. a speedy horned animal
7. the first half of the day
8. reaches out for your TV
9. sacred song
10. hard coal
11. manlike
12. bacteria killer
13. funny business
14. old stuff
15. guess and get ready
16. a tumble from expectation
17. counter time
18. counter illness
19. strong dislike
20. where men are "upside down"
21. collector of old stuff
22. out of date
23. means the opposite
24. is the opposite (55)

Autantonyms

While many words have opposites, some words are their own opposites. These autantonyms are an odd group, with two meanings that contradict one another. A butcher has a *cleaver* to *cleave* his bones; but the formal marriage ceremony bids the newly mated couple to *cleave* to one another "till death you depart." In the first case, *cleave* means *to cut clear asunder;* in the second, *to cling tight together.*

When you think better of a person, you *like* him *more;* when you think better of a proposition, you *like* it *less* or turn it down. You *trim meat* by taking the fat off; you *trim a Christmas tree* by putting ornaments on. A *fast* horse runs rapidly; a *fast* color doesn't run at all. A boat that's *fast* in getting to the dock may then be made *fast* to the dock so that it can't go anywhere else. Wind up a clock and it goes; wind up a business, and it stops. A seeded lawn has the seeds put in; a seeded raisin has the seeds taken out.

Other such self-contradictory words are *counterpart, cavalier, overlook, mortal, weather, ravel, let* (a *let* ball in tennis is one hindered by the net; Hamlet, when his friends want to stop him from following the ghost, cries, "By heaven, I'll make a ghost of him that lets me!"). Also *trip, temper, unbending, dust* (a field with insecticide or your jacket). To *dress* a fowl is to remove the feathers; when a woman *dresses,* she may put feathers on. But while *dress* and *undress* are also opposites, *to bone* means the same as *to unbone, to husk* as *to unhusk, to ravel* as *to unravel, to loose* as *to unloose, to annul* as *to disannul. To shell* is the same as *to unshell*—but *unshelled* usually means with the shells still on. *He was bested* means the same as *he was worsted.* The *inflammable* burns more quickly than the *flammable.*

Here are two games to play with autantonyms. Explain, with an example, what an autantonym is. Allow three minutes for the players to write as many as they can think of. Then each in turn gives two sentences, one for each meaning of one of his words. The one with the most correct wins.

Explain what an autantonym is, as above. Give each player three autantonyms. Each in turn gives a sentence for each of the two meanings of one of his words. A point is scored against him for each error.

Shifties

Some words, without changing their spelling, can shift their meaning and perhaps their sound as well. A *shower* of his wares put up his umbrella when a sudden *shower* came. See if you can fit the appropriate words into the blanks below. Try only four at a time. (To a group, dictate the sentences, saying "blank" where indicated. Allow three minutes to fill the blanks.) If there is a change in sound, it should be indicated. (For a short vowel, c͟a͟t; for a long vowel, cāke. For an accent, *har'ass, ref'erence.* Other changes will suggest their marking.)

1. When all the tenants complained, the landlord could not _ _ _ _ _ _ to remove the _ _ _ _ _ _. He also had to _ _ _ _ _ _ the electric-light control box.

2. The milkman was supposed to _ _ _ _ _ _ two quarts daily. The dancer bent _ _ _ _ _ _, and touched her heels.

3. _ _ _ _ upon _ _ _ _ of spectators applauded, as the _ _ _ _ of the knots shook hands with the escape artist, who had worked himself free.

4. The woman was knitting a _ _ _ _ _ _ _ sweater for her grandson. He was _ _ _ _ _ _ _ in the tennis match.

5. The friends of the _ _ _ _ _ _ runners wished they could _ _ _ _ _ _ those in front.

6. Do not shed _ _ _ _ _ because your garment _ _ _ _ _.

7. The nurse _ _ _ _ _ a bandage around the _ _ _ _ _.

8. It was such a _ _ _ _ _ _ portion that it took him less than a _ _ _ _ _ _ to consume it.

9. A _ _ _ _ _ _ of the group, lightly clad, grew _ _ _ _ _ _ and _ _ _ _ _ _ in the cold.

10. The farmer wanted to _ _ _ his seeds, but he had to stop, to chase the _ _ _, which had escaped from the sty.

11. He _ _ _ _ not want to hunt the _ _ _ _, because at this time of year they are still nursing their fawns.

12. The _ _ _ _ _ _ starts the child reading, the _ _ _ _ _ _ starts the engine going.

13. As I looked through the _ _ _ _ _ _ _ _ to the garden, the beauty was enough to _ _ _ _ _ _ _ _ me.

14. (two words) He tried to _ _ _ _ them past the _ _ _ of houses, but some ruffians stopped them; there was a _ _ _, and an angry man hit him with a _ _ _ _ pipe. (56)

There is another sort of shifting, also without any change in spelling—a shift of accent when a word is used as another part of speech. The most usual such change is of noun and verb: If you will *permit'* me to go, please write out a *per'mit*. Less often, other parts of speech are involved, as when the permit for an *in'valid* to leave the hospital turned out to be *inval'id*.

Explain this shifting, with an example. Allow three minutes for the players to write as many such words as they can. Then each in turn gives a sentence (or two), illustrating both accents of one of his words. The one with the most words correctly used wins. Here is a partial list of such shifties:

concert	escort	legate
object	combine	annex
subject	console	contact

convert	convict	progress
present	conduct	converse
concord	protest	transfer
costume	insult	incense
compound	digest	reject
absent	content	contract
repent	consort	recess

Sometimes the language shifts away from such shiftings. We have the noun *prod'uce*, the verb *produce'*; but also *product* and *production. Induct* is balanced with *induction*, but *reduce* leaps over to *reduction*. If you *frequent'* places where good English is spoken, your own slips will be less *fre'quent*.

A number of words shift their accent as their form adjusts to a different part of speech. Thus *do'cile, docil'ity; fa'cile, facil'- itate; fic'tion, ficti'tious; tel'ephone, teleph'ony, telephon'ic; fam'ily, famil'iar, familiar'ity; con'template, contem'plative, contempla'tion.* Also *refer', ref'erence; infer', in'ference, in- feren'tial.* There are also *in'fluence* and *influen'tial*, but there is no word *influe* (although you can be *up* the *flue*—and of course, there was the boy who opened the window and *in- fluenza). Maniac* and *zodiac* become *mani͞'acal, zodi͞'acal.*

Double Words

Many words, far from changing their sound, repeat it. Not only the infant enjoys the repetitive chime. The reduplicative words appear in three main varieties:

1. Exact repetition, both parts the same: *bonbon, cancan, ack-ack.*

2. The initial sound changes: *hodgepodge, even stephen, blackjack, jeepers creepers.*

3. The vowel changes: *chitchat, pitter-patter, Ping-Pong.*

In a few cases, the final sound holds the expression together: *pish tush, whippersnapper.*

In three minutes, the players write as many such words as they can. The player with the most words reads them. Cancel all words anyone else has. The one with the most words no one else has begins, each in turn giving a sentence that shows he knows how to use the expression. The one with the most correct wins.

Here are some reduplicative terms, grouped as listed above (exact repetition makes the smallest class):

1.

chin-chin	bye-bye	ta-ta
goody-goody	pooh-pooh	tut-tut

2.

okeydokey	teeny-weeny	hotsy-totsy
boogie-woogie	hokey-pokey	hurdy-gurdy
honky-tonk	roly-poly	nitwit
hocus-pocus	abracadabra	walkie-talkie
willy-nilly	lovey-dovey	super-duper
niminy-piminy	hurly-burly	namby-pamby
ragtag	claptrap	boohoo
harum-scarum	mumbo jumbo	hanky-panky
razzle-dazzle	bowwow	heebie-jeebies

3.

ticktock	hippety-hoppety	tittle-tattle
seesaw	wishy-washy	riffraff
zigzag	tickletackle	creepy-crawly
shilly-shally	mishmash	flimflam
jimjams	fiddle-faddle	topsy-turvy
knickknack	gewgaw	dingdong

Irreversibles

An elephant, you know, can have fleas, but a flea cannot have elephants. Such a condition is called irreversible. There are also words that are irreversible; that is, if you turn their parts around, they have quite different meanings. You do not have to *understand* the laws of gravity when you *stand under* a shower. The water will come down on you just the same. You will be *inundated,* and that's a good situation to be *undated in.* You would rather live on a *houseboat* than in a *boathouse.*

Each player writes two pairs of Irreversibles, then writes a sentence for each member of each pair. Sentences are read aloud, and the group decides which are most effective or most amusing.

There are various relations between the members of a pair of irreversibles. Sometimes they are close. You can ask someone to "come out and play," but you can also ask, "How did things come out?" which *is* reversible with "the outcome." Usually, however, there is a greater difference, as when you *overlook* an error or *look over* a work to find any errors. Sometimes the two words have no relation at all, as the roadway *overpass* and the holy day *Passover,* or when *inure* turns out to turn into *urine.*

Here are some true irreversibles to play with:

outright, right out	inhere, herein
withhold, hold with	overcome, come over
withdraw, draw with	outlet, let out
income, come in	downright, right down
outrun, run out	overtake, take over
outjump, jump out	outlook, look out
outtalk, talk out	underbrush, brush under
overdone, done over	underground, ground under
undergo, go under	outplayed, played out
withstand, stand with	overwork, work over
overrule, rule over	overhand, hand over
underwrite, write under	overreach, reach over
overtime, time over	outboard, board out
instep, step in (in step)	oversee, see over
overact, act over	hangover, overhang
oversleep, sleep over	

A player gives an irreversible and points. The player pointed at must at once give a sentence using *the other member* of the pair. Then he gives a word and points at another player, and so on. A point off if a player takes more than ten seconds to start his sentence or uses the term wrongly. When you stop, the player with fewest points against him wins.

You can find almost any sort of wordplay in *Alice in Wonderland.* The irreversibles pop up too. "Do cats eat bats? Do bats eat cats?" Later, the March Hare tells Alice: "You should say what you mean." She replies: "I do; at least, I mean what I say; that's the same thing." The Hatter interrupts: "Not a bit! You might as well say that 'I see what I eat' is the same thing as 'I eat what I see'!" When you *eat over* at a friend's house, try not to *overeat.*

Euphemy

With the great variety of words in our language, it should be simple to select words that please. Way back in Bible days (Proverbs 15:1) it was remarked that "a soft answer turneth away wrath." The telephone company means the same thing when it observes that the voice with the smile wins.

It is therefore natural to try to choose pleasant words for unpleasant subjects. Down the years, a *burier* was turned into an *undertaker;* now he is likely to be called a *mortician.* And of course, no one has *false teeth* anymore. If there are just a few, you wear a *bridge;* if it's a mouthful, top or bottom, you have a *plate.* Or you have new *dentures.*

When the word *opium* acquired a bad reputation, pushers found it more pleasant to promote a derivative of opium they called *morphine,* after Morpheus, the god of dreams. A concentrated form of this is *diamorphine,* but who wants to *die o' morphine?* So, lo and behold, it is on the underworld market with the attractive name of *heroin.* Such glossing over of unsavory things is called euphemy.

A euphemism may result from a prim social attitude, as when the Victorians, with ground-sweeping skirts, spoke of the *limbs* of a table. Euphemisms are also often employed for commercial reasons, as when the vegetable extract butterine was renamed *oleomargarine,* then just *margarine,* which sounds like a girl's name, and comes from the Greek word for *pearl.* (The Association of Butterine Manufacturers voted that the *g* in margarine should be given the *j* sound, as in a *gem.)*

In everyday speech, there are frequent occasions when a euphemism comes in handy. For instance, if someone you like seems a bit slow, you may more kindly say that he likes to be sure before he goes ahead. Don't tell a woman that her face would stop a clock. Say to her: "Every time I look at you, time stands still."

Euphemakem

For each of the following words—take only four at a time—write a sentence *not using that word* but conveying the idea in a more friendly fashion. For a group, all take the same word, and see whose sentence is the most effective. Then the next word.

shrewd	stingy	cunning
sarcastic	greedy	weak-willed
stupid	dull	timid
garrulous	boisterous	impudent
pigheaded	hot-tempered	conceited

When my sons were little, I told them that if someone jostled them on a crowded street, they should say, "I'm sorry." Notice, that's an unfinished remark. It may mean, "I'm sorry you didn't look where you were going"—or various other things. But the soft answer turneth away wrath.

7

HOMONYMS, HOMONIMBLES;
KNOCK, KNOCK,
BUT NEVER LAUGH!

Here are the homonyms! Hosts of words in our language, without any relation of meaning, happen to look or sound alike. (There are even more in Chinese, but they are harder to write.) Homonyms may be a source of confusion, or they may be a source of fun.

Here are just a handful:

boarder, border	coward, cowered, cowherd
tease, teas, t's	break, brake
here, hear	wither, whither
watt, what	stare, stair
real, reel	pervade, purveyed
quarts, quartz	subtler, sutler
ate, eight	plum, plumb
tare, tear	reed, read
red, read	neigh, nay
great, grate	pores, pours
swayed, suede	paws, pause
rays, raze, raise	time, thyme
air, ere, e'er, heir	chaste, chased
meat, mete, meet	pier, peer
knight, night	suite, sweet
sale, sail	martial, marshal
knead, need, kneed	bear, bare
assent, ascent	metal, mettle
missile, missal	wined, whined, wind
better, bettor	core, corps
idle, idol, idyll	feat, feet

pedal, peddle	way, weigh
borough, burro, burrow	choir, quire
aloud, allowed	foul, fowl
vain, vein	team, teem
there, their, they're	ball, bawl
bow, bough	rapt, wrapped, rapped
council, counsel	paced, paste
canon, cannon	rain, rein, reign
vary, very	stationery, stationary
cymbal, symbol	dough, doe, do (in music)
feign, fain, fane	hoes, hose, ho's
caret, carat, carrot	bowl, bole, boll
cereal, serial	

Several games can be played with homonyms.

Every player writes all the homonyms he can think of in three minutes. Score ten points for the most. For every set no one else has, ten points. For other sets, total players minus the number that have the set. For example, if six are playing and three have *tare, tear,* award three points each. For sets with more than two homonyms, two points for each word over two. Highest score wins.

Each player writes two sets of homonyms. Exchange papers. Each writes sentences using the homonyms on the sheet he now has. Group decides which sentences are most effective or most amusing.

Many words, without changing spelling or sound, have several meanings. Thus *tip* may mean *to tilt, the very top, a hint, extra pay for service.* Lawyers and drinkers both go to the *bar,* unless persons *bar* their way. A few more such words are:

bore	bank	gorge	till
bowl	jam	perch	bark
hold	crane	bit	court
rake	punch	rail	shed
steep	score	lay	net
keen	pulse	flatter	husband
cow	bully	ring	sole
trial	limp	can	post
hops	fair	fan	set
fare	slip	wear	redress
desert	graze	fleet	chest
rear	box	row	fuse
saw	bat	crow	tenor
drove	stage	tie	terms
brief	palm	down	hose

Notice that by far the most of these are one-syllable words from the Anglo-Saxon. These have been in the language a long time, gradually developing various meanings. One word that has recently developed a new sense is *bit*. In addition to *a small piece, the cutting edge of a tool, the interchangeable cutting point of a drill, the metal mouthpiece of a horse's bridle, the past tense of bite,* etc., *bit* is now used to mean a *b*inary dig*it*, a number in the system of counting used for a computer.

Each player writes two words, each of which has more than one meaning. Exchange papers. For the words you now have, write sentences for as many meanings as you can think of. Each reads in turn. Score two points for every correct sentence; one point off for every wrong meaning; one off for every proper meaning not used. Group decides whether a meaning is "proper"; omitting far-out or little-used meanings need not bring a penalty.

Homonyms, often humorous ones, may also be formed by breaking a word apart. *Scintillate* then becomes *sin till late; ingratiate* informs you that *in gray she ate.* A *nocturne* becomes a *knocked urn.* You probably remember the fruity remark: "We're too young, dear, we canteloupe" (can't elope). Thus also *mountebank, cancel, ideal.* Even some of our states have been torn apart. Did *Ida hoe* the cornfield? *Alaska* (I'll ask her). How do you like my *new jersey?* The tenor was hit in the eye last night; can the *Tennessee?*

Give an example of these nimble homonyms, or homonimbles. In three minutes, players write sentences with the "nimble" form of words they think of. Group decides which are cleverest.

If players have difficulty thinking of such words, point out that an easy break is to pull away the letter *a. Attempting* this can be *a tempting* pastime. Thus *avoid* becomes *a void;* similarly you can *adjust a just* measure, make *abasement a basement.* Thus, too, *aboard, abound, about, abridge, acclaim, ac-*

count, accrue (a crew), adjudge, adore, affair, again, ahead, alone, abase, anneal (an eel), and more.

Give the players just one example of this, and let them have another go. If they've been doing all right with the nimbles, make the *a* drop a separate game.

Under the Sheet

One homonym game has been played for generations, using various catchphrases; perhaps the most popular is Under the Sheet. One player goes out of the room. The rest agree on a set of homonyms, or one word with several meanings. The first player returns, and asks a question of each player in turn. Each must answer using one meaning of the chosen word—but instead of saying the word, he says "under the sheet." The first player must guess the word as quickly as he can. When he does, another player goes out, and a new word is chosen. Repeat until all have been out. A penalty of a half-minute is added for every wrong guess; the player with the least total time wins.

Suppose the word chosen is *deck.* A possible sequence is:

> Question: What did you do last Sunday?
> Answer: I wanted to shuffle the under the sheet, but couldn't get anyone to play.
> Question: And you?
> Answer: I wanted to under the sheet my hat, but I didn't have the right color ribbon.
> Question: What did you eat for dinner?
> Answer: My friend arrived on the ship from France today, so I went to the cabin under the sheet with her, and looked at the menu.

And so on, until the player guesses *deck.*

Take five sentences at a time. Fill in the blanks with the appropriate homonyms. The first to finish receives five points, second four points, third two points, fourth one point. For any mistake or blank, two points off.

A

1. The shoemaker _ _ _ _ him a pair of rubber _ _ _ _ _ shoes.
2. Asked if he _ _ _ _ _ for them, they would not _ _ _ _ _ _ him, but cried that he _ _ _ _ _ on them.
3. _ _ _ _ over the _ _ _ _ and try to see the camera that fell into the water.
4. All _ _ _ _ turned on the chairman as he announced the vote: "The _ _ _ _ have it."
5. The farmer taught his _ _ _ to make hay while the _ _ _ shines.
6. He shook the _ _ _ _ _ to speed up the horse: "Let's get home before it _ _ _ _ _!"
7. He went out to _ _ _ the field, to make enough money _ _ that his wife would not have to _ _ _ her own dresses.
8. A _ _ _ _ _ was not enough paper to set down all the music for the _ _ _ _ _.
9. He visited the Kurds; they had milked the mares and soured the milk; and he was amused at the _ _ they _ _ _ _ _ their _ _ _ _.
10. The _ _ _ _ _ young bride was delighted with the honeymoon _ _ _ _ _ in the luxurious hotel.

B

1. In colder _ _ _ _ _ _ the mountaineer had made many more difficult _ _ _ _ _ _.
2. He knew at once, from the smiling face, which _ _ _ had _ _ _ the election.
3. See how everyone _ _ _ _ _ _ at the cinema star as she makes her grand entrance down the _ _ _ _ _ _!
4. The long tramp in the _ _ _ weather served only to _ _ _ _ his appetite.
5. He _ _ _ _ as though greeting a lady, as he goes under the low _ _ _ _ _ _.
6. Too often the _ _ _ _ _ _ of the church are thrust aside for the _ _ _ _ _ _ _ of war.
7. Despite the _ _ _ _ _ safe and the automatic alarm, they managed to _ _ _ _ _ the bonds.
8. He had _ _ _ _ _ _ _ enough to recognize that they were trying to _ _ _ _ _ _ him to rebellion.
9. In the cathedral you are not _ _ _ _ _ _ _ to speak _ _ _ _ _.
10. The _ _ _ _ of the sun were too hot for them to _ _ _ _ the old building, so that they could _ _ _ _ _ the dome of the new capitol.
(57)

You may enjoy making up more sentences of this kind for further play.

First player gives a homonym and points. The player pointed to must at once give a sentence (or sentences) using the different meanings of the given word. Then he gives a word and points, and so on. For not starting in five seconds, take one point off. Also, one point off for an error, or for omitting a meaning when there are more than two, as *rain, reign, rein.*

In three minutes, players write the most amusing sentences they can, using homonyms. The group decides which are cleverest. For example:

Did the *wheelwright write* the *right rite?*
The whistle *too*ted at *two.* I heard it from *two* to *two* to *two two too.*
When the bright *night* faded, was the slight *knight* jaded?
Before the *idle idol,* he realized the lovers' *ideal idyll.*

If you were a Roman, you'd have a hard time beating the fourfold Latin homonym *Malo malo malo malo.* It can be translated:

> I'd rather be in an apple tree
> Than an evil man in adversity.

(The Roman went roamin' all over Europe. In England he left campsites and a magic square. See Chapters 8 and 11.)

Homonimbles

Homonyms and synonyms can be used nimbly—a *yarn*'s a *thread,* a *yarn*'s a *tale,* and thereby hangs a *tail!* Bypassing any literal restraint of common sense, employing instead your sense of humor and lively leap of imagination and flick of fancy, you may work nimbly with familiar words and arrive at strange conclusions. You can employ what logicians call the law of the undistributed middle—and that doesn't mean that your father can put on extra weight! By these rules, a rhapsodist may turn out to be a shipping clerk, and a pathologist a scoutmaster.

Here you can walk in Alice's Wonderland again, as the Mock Turtle explains: "We called him Tortoise because he taught us."

Two homonimbles have already become classics.

1. Why is a sheet of ruled paper like a lazy dog? A *ruled sheet* is an *ink-lined plane*. An *inclined plane* is a *slope up*. A *slow pup* is a lazy dog.

2. How did a man get out of a solid, completely sealed house, with nothing in it but himself and a table, in the middle of a forest? He rubbed his hands until they were *sore*. Then he proceeded to *saw* the table in half. *Two halves* make a *whole*. He crawled through the *hole,* shouted until he was *hoarse,* and galloped away. This has been winning chuckles for nigh on a century, and was sprung on me just the other day by a nine-year-old.

Let's try a spate of homonimbles. A good start is with a *pretty girl*. A *pretty girl*'s a *belle*. A *bell*'s a *ringer*. A *ringer*'s a *dinner* (noise maker). A *dinner*'s a *meal. Meal* is *flour. Flowers* for the *pretty girl.*

We got to that pretty quickly. The trick is to go along as nimbly as you can, until you come to what seems a happy ending. Then you form a question that fits the nimbling, and put the question first: "What shall we get for a pretty girl?"

Let's try another: What did the man wear when, being hungry at midnight, he went to the *icebox?* A *nice box* is one with *candy. Candy*'s a *sweetmeat. A sweet meet* is a *gathering of pretty girls. Pretty girls* are *belles.* (A different route, this time!) A *bell* is for *diving. Diving*'s a *sport.* A *sport* is a *gay blade.* A *blade* is *grass. Grass* becomes *hay. Hey* is an *exclamation.* An *exclamation* marks *surprise. Surprise* is *to catch unawares. Unawear*'s what the man had on when he went to the *icebox.*

Pretty bad? Shall we venture one more? What shall we do with a man who wants a bribe? A *bribe* is a *consent rate. Concentrate* is *to think; to think* is *to reckon; to reckon* is *to figure.* A *figure* is a *shape. Shape* is *to fashion. Fashion* is *style; a stile* is a *gate; a gait* is a *pace; a pace* is a *walk.* Tell him to take a *walk.*

Explain homonimbles to the group, with an example. Then give them five minutes to write one flow of nimbles. If they prefer, give them overnight, and have each bring his best nimble to the next gathering. For a few months, a while back, I exchanged nimbles with a friend by postcard. They must have given the postman some puzzled reading!

While homonimbles and synonimbles make games, they may be played as a part of serious doings. Film star Shirley Mac-Laine recalls that the first time she was acting in a film under the famous director Alfred Hitchcock, she was naturally nervous. Hitchcock said to her: "Genuine chopper, old girl!" When Shirley looked bewildered, he said, "Try some synonyms." When she reached *real* for *genuine* and *ax* for *chopper,* he nodded: "That's it: *real ax, relax,* old girl!" Laughing, she did. She added, "He has millions of these."

Linked with the nimbles, though briefer, are the semantic antics of descriptions set in two rhyming words. Daffy definitions have been put into several books, one called *Felt Smelt,* a title that should entertain a fishmonger. Many such definitions are far-fetched, but *teeny bikini* is neat for a *fig leaf,* and a *nasal appraisal* could fittingly warn you of the proximity of a *skunk.* The trick has been popular with columnists and TV comedians, and has had wide circulation under the malodorous name of Stinky Pinky, but it is by no means new. Jonathan Swift, in the early eighteenth century, turned the phrases: "I'm hot, are you a Scot?" "I'm cold, are you a scold?" Yet it continues. I have heard six-year-olds bidding farewell: "See you later, alligator!" "In a while, crocodile!" And more. Sometime when you're bored with what the family insists on watching on television, try this way of spreading a *humor rumor* or two. Another variety is in Chapter 15.

Just this afternoon I saw a sign on the back of an automobile:

> See You Later—Overtaker.
> In a Casket—Crazy Basket.

Don't rush your days away.

Knock, Knock!

You know the next steps:

> Who's there?
> Anna.
> Anna who?
> Anna gonna tellya.

A few years back, at any momentary pause in the conversation, someone was sure to call out: "Knock, knock." And, oh, the poor names that suffered twisting!

> Adolph who?
> A dolphin diving to murmur a mermaid's name.
>
> Abigail who?
> A big gale swept over the tossing ship and drowned me.
>
> Ariadna who?
> 'Arry add 'nother log to the fire.
>
> Yolanda who?
> Yolanda big fish if you have the right bait.
>
> Mary who?
> Merry Christmas, and try to do better in the New Year!

Back in 1820, the game went this way:

> Knock, knock [actually, with a cane].
> Who's there?
> Buff.
> What says Buff?

Buff (the knocker) says the most absurd things he can think of to make the others laugh. When one finally cannot keep a straight face, Buff stands in front of him and recites:

> Buff neither laughs nor smiles
> But looks in your face
> With a comical grace
> And delivers the staff to you, sir!

Whereupon the laugher takes the cane and becomes the Buff.
And this game is traceable back to 1611, when a dictionary held
the definition: "buff . . . to burst out in laughter." The fellow
who tried to get you to laugh in the 1960's didn't know that he
was upholding three and a half centuries of comic tradition.
And lest you think the tradition dead, while I was working on
this book in September, 1970, a ten-year-old came over to me,
and said: "Knock, knock."

> Who's there?
> Boo.
> Boo who?
> Don't cry!

For men may come and men may go, but games go on
forever. Turn the page gently.

8

ROOTS AND RECRUITS:
GAPS IN OUR LANGUAGE,
TELESCOPES, ROOT 'EM OUT,
LANGUAGES MADE TO ORDER

English dictionaries contain many more words than those of other languages. The French Academy dictionary has fewer than 300,000 words, whereas our Webster's Unabridged has well over 600,000. Two reasons account for this. One reason is that, while the Greeks, for example, scorned barbarian tongues, and the Spanish sought to maintain the "purity" of their Castilian, the English have always borrowed freely. Wherever our explorers, soldiers, missionaries, and traders went, they came back not only with new objects but with new words. Another, more fundamental, reason is that the language we speak is a combination of two large family groups. One has come down to us from Latin, the language of the ancient Romans. Some of these words were borrowed directly at various times—and a number from the Greek as well—but a large portion came via the Norman French, brought over by William the Conqueror in 1066. Virtually 99 percent of all French words come from the Latin. The other family group is the Germanic, spoken by the Anglo-Saxons when they invaded England in the fifth century.

The Romans first went to England, looking for conquest and tin, in the century before Christ, and remained for about five hundred years. But they remained an army of hostile conquer-ors. They built superb roads, some still used today, so that their armies could move swiftly, and they established many camps. In our language, the main relics of this occupation are place names. The Latin word for camp is *castrum;* in different parts of England local accents changed this to *caster, chester,* or *cester.* Thus you can live today in Lancaster or Westchester. An early Celtic region, site of a Roman camp, later became a Saxon county *(shire).* It is best known in America today—Worcestershire—as the name of a sauce.

Other Latin and Greek words came into English through church activity, through the literary and philosophical stir of the Renaissance, and in the development of science. New words today in medicine and other fields are often taken from the classical languages.

When the Norman French conquered the Saxons, the Normans naturally became the privileged overlords. One effect of this on the language is noted by Sir Walter Scott in his novel *Ivanhoe.* The jester and the swineherd remark that when animals are alive and have to be tended, they are plain Saxon *bull, calf, sheep, pig;* but when they are cooked and served at table, they are haughty Norman *beef, veal, mutton, pork.*

The Norman children, however, were tended by Saxon nurses, so that for the first five or six years of their lives, the young ones heard mainly Saxon words. Thus it happens that most of the simpler words of our language—the structural words, *be, of, from, to,* and the everyday words, *home, dress, bread, butter, milk*—are of Saxon, Germanic, origin. We often have two words meaning about the same thing; the Germanic word will seem closer to the heart and the hearth, the word from the Latin will seem less emotional, more intellectual. The French *fraternité* means the brotherhood of man; the English word *fraternity* makes us think of a secret society. *Motherhood* is a blessing, *maternity* is a hospital ward. A *hearty* welcome is more hearty than a *cordial* reception; *friendship* is more friendly than *amity. Happiness* is closer to our spirits than *felicity.* A well is *deep;* our learning may be *profound.*

It has been said that while Latin words are the building blocks of the language, Saxon words are the mortar. You can get along quite well without the Roman vocabulary. The poet Edna St. Vincent Millay wrote the book of an opera, *The King's Henchman,* using words only from the Anglo-Saxon, nothing that came into the language after the Norman conquest. *But it would be* difficult *indeed to write anything without words from the* conquered *Saxons.* (I have italicized the Saxon words in this sentence. Change *difficult* to *hard,* and *conquered* to *beaten,* and who is the conqueror now?) More than once—the Greeks did it to the Romans—the conquered race had its triumph on the tongue.

Discriminate

We have, therefore, a wide choice of words in English, and may distinguish a delicate shade of meaning or feeling or tone by choosing a word of Germanic or of Latin origin. Here is a very short list to show the difference. In each pair, the first word is Germanic, the second Latin:

help—assist	ask—inquire	brave—courageous
want—desire	smell—odor	toothpaste—dentifrice
enough—sufficient	stop—cease	sweat—perspire
try—endeavor	hide—conceal	get—obtain
true—veritable	show—evince	buy—purchase
meal—repast	live—reside	drink—imbibe, beverage
read—peruse	begin—initiate	building—edifice

Sometimes we have triplets, as with *lawful, legal, loyal; kingly, regal, royal.* In both these cases, the first word is from the Anglo-Saxon, the second directly from the Latin, the third from the Latin via the French.

Give one or two examples of this diversity from the list above. In three minutes players write as many pairs as they can, of a simple word and a more "learned" word. Read them aloud. If any question arises, check in the dictionary. Player with the most good pairs wins.

Write sentences for three such pairs of words, so that the word will fit the tone. For example: He *hid* the bicycle behind the bush. When he stood before the college director of admissions, he tried to *conceal* his nervousness.

Players read their sentences aloud; the group decides which are the most effective. As a variation, all the players can be given the same three pairs of words.

Occasionally we use a Saxon word for one part of speech, one from the Latin for a less frequently spoken part. For example (Saxon first):

finger—digital	see—visible	above, better—superiority
breast—pectoral	hear—audible	handle—manipulate
kin—familial	feel—sensitive	handy—manual
ball—spheroid	eye—ocular	much—quantity
smell—olfactory, nasal	handmade—manufactured*	

Doublets

In quite a large number of cases, one original source by divers diverse devious paths has given us more than one current word. Such words—*flour* and *flower; genteel, gentle, gentile,* and *jaunty; praise* and *price*—are called doublets. Here are just a few:

abbreviate, abridge	aggravate, aggrieved
esteem, estimate, aim	alloy, ally
aptitude, attitude	blame, blaspheme
chance, cadence	poor, pauper
treason, tradition	assemble, assimilate
astound, astonish, stun	etiquette, ticket
dainty, dignity	dauphin, dolphin
employ, imply	fact, feat
faculty, facility	kennel, channel, canal
lace, lasso	chattel, cattle, capital
cavalry, chivalry	charge, cargo
glamour, grammar	flask, fiasco
naïve, native	monetary, monitory
musket, mosquito	onion, union
patron, pattern	potion, poison
raid, road	ration, reason, ratio
rover, robber	sergeant, servant
scandal, slander	scout, auscultate
secure, sure	supervisor, surveyor
tamper, temper	vast, waste
respect, respite	quiet, quit, quite, coy
disc, discus, disk, dish, dais, desk	

Write sentences for three sets of doublets, showing that you know their different meanings. (Do not pick the easy ones.)

*Literally, this means made by hand, but now the hand usually operates a machine.

Although words, on the whole, have been fairly fixed in their meanings, a number have shifted considerably from their earliest sense. Look, for instance, at the word *prevent*. It is formed from the Latin prefix *pre-*, meaning *before*, and a form of the Latin root *ven*, meaning *come*. In 1548, the Book of Common Prayer printed the exhortation: "Prevent us, O Lord, in all our doings!" meaning *Come before us, and pave the way.* Alas, in the practical world of our daily doings, the fellow that comes before us is more likely to take the best things himself, and prevent us (in the present sense) from getting what we desire. In a similar way, because of our lackadaisical forefathers, the word *presently*, which first meant *at the present moment*, came to mean *after a while.* (It has regained its original sense in such weather reports as "It is presently cool and clear.") Still a greater change came upon our word *silly*, which (as its German form *selig* still does) used to mean *blessed*.

Scientific words have to be precise, and are less likely to change their meaning. Many of them—of the more recently isolated chemical elements, of botanical terms, diseases, mathematical relations—are formed from the name of the person who found or first described the thing they name. *Galvanize* comes from Luigi Galvani, who in 1792 developed the direct current (galvanic) battery. A. M. Ampère, Madame Curie, Michael Faraday, William Konrad Roentgen, C. A. de Coulomb, Hans Geiger—men as far back as the thirteenth-century Leonardo Fibonacci have given their names to science. Crisp, blunt one-syllable words are lively elements in our speech. Several new ones have come in through the accident of a scientist's name: *ohm, watt, volt, mach.*

Other words taken from names have gone into the vocabularies of various fields.

Read aloud the following names (five at a time). Give the players time, after each, to write the English word derived from the name. In a few cases, more than one word has come from the name.

1. Amerigo Vespucci, Italian explorer and mapmaker
2. Jupiter Ammon, chief of the ancient gods

3. Atlas, mythological giant, condemned to hold the earth on his shoulders
4. Ceres, Roman goddess of the harvest
5. Joachimsthal, valley in Germany where silver was mined
6. Joseph I. Guillotin, French physician
7. Hamburg, city in Germany
8. Iris, Greek messenger of the gods, changed by jealous Juno into the rainbow
9. Julius Caesar, Roman commander
10. Augustus Caesar, first Roman emperor
11. Antoine J. Sax, musican
12. Vulcan, blacksmith of the Roman gods
13. Frankfurt, a city in Germany
14. Mars, the Roman god of war
15. Limousin, a province of old France (58)

Below is a list of English words from names. Give players five at a time. They are to write the name from which the word came. (If this proves too hard, reverse the process, and play as above.)

1. meander
2. bayonet
3. tarantula
4. hector
5. bloomers
6. bronze
7. cravat
8. cupidity
9. currant
10. ermine
11. hermetically
12. jovial
13. magnet
14. marcel (wave)
15. maudlin
16. mayonnaise
17. milliner
18. ogre
19. panic
20. quixotic
21. sandwich
22. spaniel
23. spinach
24. tangerine
25. peach (59)

Other words derived from names include: valentine, kilowatt, gun, artesian, derby, echo, gardenia, lilliputian, rhinestone, spruce (the tree)—and a fifth of the chemical elements: alabamine, cobalt, columbium, gadolinium, gallium, germanium, hafnium, holmium, indium, nickel, palladium, polonium, rhenium, ruthenium, scandium, strontium, tantalum, thorium, thulium, titanium, vanadium, virginium.

Even the name of a nation can give a language words, often through rivalry. Thus what the English call *taking French leave* (AWOL), the French, retorting, call *filer à l'Anglais.* Our biggest collection of such words grew in the years of discovery and colonization of the New World. For over a century the English and the Dutch were rivals. Dutch vessels bore a broomstick on their mastheads, as a sign that they swept the seas. Sometimes they borrowed an English commander: Henry Hudson, when he discovered the river that bears his name, was flying the Dutch flag, and the city founded on Manhattan Island (bought from the Indians with twenty-four dollars worth of trinkets) was called New Amsterdam.

The English responded by calling a lot of things they held in contempt "Dutch."

Dutchies

Give the example everyone knows: Dutch treat—which is no treat at all, for everyone pays for himself. In three minutes, players write as many Dutchies as they can. Then they use each in a sentence, ready to explain its meaning.

Dictate Dutchies, three at a time. Players write sentences using them and should be ready to explain their meaning. Here are the main ones:

1. Dutch auction	8. Dutch feast	15. Dutch wife
2. Dutch anchor	9. Dutch gold	16. talk like a Dutch uncle
3. Dutchman's breeches	10. Dutch luck	17. I'll be a Dutchman
4. Dutch bargain	11. Dutch nightingale	18. in Dutch
5. Dutch comfort	12. Dutch concert	19. double Dutch
6. Dutch courage	13. Dutch praise	20. Dutchman's land (60)
7. Dutch defense	14. Dutch reckoning	

Words keep coming into our language as new needs arise. We had the word *zip,* an echoic word (one that sounds like what it means) for a noise like a sudden rip or swift movement. In the 1930's a new type of fastener was patented that works with one swift pull: naturally, it is the *zipper.* "Will you please zip me?" is a wife's frequent dressing call. And now Uncle Sam has taken over the word, using the *zip code* to expedite delivery of mail. We have another echoic word, *whiz,* for things that go whizzing by. But the bright lads who were the *whiz kids* of radio and TV contests took their name by a shortening of *wizard,* familiar from *The Wizard of Oz. Radar, television, proton, jet plane,* and *laser* are just a few of the well-known words created in the twentieth century to name new substances, instruments, ideas, and forces science is developing for us.

Many more specialized new words, for chemicals, medicines, and species of plants and insects, will never find their way into even the largest general dictionary. Like *quaquaversal,* a geologists' term, they are understood by specialists only. If such a term becomes of general interest, it is usually identified by an abbreviation, or by initials like TNT, ACTH, DNA, and more. *Googol* is a word a mathematician coined to mean one followed by a hundred zeros.

Write five words or initial names that have come into existence during your lifetime. Then write a sentence for each, showing that you know how to use it. Score ten for each word no one else has. For other words, score the number in the group minus the number of those that have it. Deduct one for every wrong word or word wrongly used in a sentence. The highest score wins.

The period of by far the greatest word innovation in England was the reign of good Queen Bess. In that Elizabethan period, writers proudly presented new words, which their rivals promptly attacked. Thus Thomas Nash, who coined the unsuccessful word *carminist* for *songwriter,* in 1592 gnashed his teeth over Gabriel Harvey's suggestions of *conscious, jovial, rascality, notoriety,* and *extensively,* all of which have survived. Another writer, Puttenham, three years earlier boasted of having made up *scientific, idiom, methodical, savage, audacious, numerosity, implete,* and *politien,* only the last three of which have failed to meet lasting favor. Ben Jonson in his play *The Poetaster* (1601) satirizes a rival playwright, John Marston, making him spew out the words *retrograde, damp, strenuous, spurious, defunct, clumsy, prorump, obstupefact, ventositous.*

The richest word man of this, or of any, period was William Shakespeare. Of the 17,677 words in his writings, over 1,700 were written first by him. Among these are:

aerial	auspicious	assassination
barefaced	bump	castigate
clangor	critic	critical
compunctious	conflux	countless

denote	eventful	what the dickens
dwindle	foppish	exposure
fair play	gibber	fancy-free
fretful	homekeeping	gnarled
hurry	laughable	impartial
lapse	misplaced	leapfrog
lonely	perusal	monumental
pedant	seamy	road
savagery	sportive	sprightful

How many of the above words are new to you? Look them up. Write sentences for up to five of them, showing that you know their meanings. Don't pick the easy ones!

Shakespeare also delighted in forming new words with affixes. He added to the language *ensnare, ensear, enmesh, enfreedom, ensky; dishearten, disbench, disedge, dispark; recall, respeak, reword; fitful, changeful, distrustful, disgraceful, spleenful; sapless, countless, dateless,* to name but a few. Along some of these paths he occasionally went too far. In *Othello* he speaks of "traitors ensteeped to enclog the guiltless keel." And, while he did coin the useful word *gloomy,* in *A Midsummer Night's Dream,* he reached out for *brisky, spheery, barry,* and *barky.* But without the words Shakespeare created, English would be immeasurably poorer.

The use of affixes, which gave a superb flavor to Elizabethan English, has not died out. Our fathers matched Shakespeare's *heaven-kissing* hills with *skyscraper* buildings. We can prefix *re-* and *anti-* and *super-,* to form words like *reentry, anticommunist, supermarket.* At our airports, *loudspeakers* (these two words are also new) call for passengers *em*planing or *de*planing. *Wise* has come into vogue again as a suffix. Lewis Carroll used *contrariwise;* we slip into *costumewise, costwise,* and almost anything *wise* or *otherwise.*

Some of the words coined in the centuries after Elizabeth I seem destined to remain buried in the old dictionaries. Who would think of calling a man *chaetophorous* when he needs a shave? Or of sending to the *zythepsary* (brewery) for a case of beer? He would be branded a highfalutin *pseudosopher* and a complete bore. It is also hard to imagine calling a fluent liar *mendaciloquent,* or taking a *pediluvium* (footbath). How many men ask for a *eupyrion* to light their pipes? Or look for an *opaion,* to let out the smoke? One would rather, like King James I, write *A Counterblast to Tobacco!*

Writers in earlier times also recognized that words would fade away. Pope said, in 1729:

> Think we that modern words eternal are?
> Toupet and tompion, cosins, and colmar
> Hereafter will be called by some plain man
> A wig, a watch, a pair of stays, a fan.

Pope has one wrong on each list. He could not know that, after almost 250 years, the toupet (toupee) would be in style again, or that one of the first things from which women would be "liberated" were the stays (which many today will not recognize as whalebone corsets). Byron, a hundred years after Pope, expressed the idea more generally:

> As forests shed their foliage by degrees,
> So fade expressions which in season please.

Some of the forgotten words, however, seem to deserve a better fate. Many American housewives, for example, might be reproached for their *emacity (itch to be buying).* Others, no doubt, may properly exclaim: "My helpmate? He's my hindermate!" It might comfort some policemen to be able to refer to *ochlocracy* for *mob rule. Chasmin* seems a good word for a *slow, wide yawn*—such as I hope this book is not inducing. Further journeying along this path can use as a guide my *Dictionary of Early English.*

Most of our coinages sort of slipped into the language as the occasion called them into being. But the Elizabethan practice of deliberately inventing words has also continued. About 1640, the Dutch chemist Jan Baptista von Helment made up the word *gas,* saying he got the form from the word *chaos,* used by the doctor and alchemist Theophrastus Bombastus von Hohenheim, better known in later years as Paracelsus. Bombastus himself, a hundred years earlier, had coined *sylph, gnome,* and *zinc.* In 1790 the English Jeremy Bentham argued for the deliberate creation of words, and made up *dynamic, international, exhaustive, maximize, minimize.* A valuable new word was added in 1840, when William Whewell wrote, in *The Philosophy of the Inductive Sciences:* "We very much need a name to describe a cultivator of science in general. I should incline to call him a scientist." It seems strange that the word *scientist* is little more than 130 years old. Perhaps we should have celebrated its anniversary!

About 1890, the word *Kodak* was coined by the Eastman Company, as a trade name for their portable camera (*camera obscura* was late Latin for *dark box*). It was their private name until general use made it another word for *camera.* Manufacturers today go to odd ends in the search for attractive names for their products; the international chemical firm of Pfizer had a computer supply them with a list of 45,000 possible names.

There is no doubt that English, rich as it is, can use some new words. Evidence of this is the large number of words we still borrow, such as *intelligentsia* from Russia, *blasé* from France. Some of these borrowings, like *garage, liaison, bizarre, role, regime, employee,* have been fully adopted into the language. Others, like *ennui, malaise, Zeitgeist, Weltanschauung, protégé, fiancée, naïveté,* still retain a foreign flavor, like recent immigrants.

In three minutes players write as many recent word immigrants as they can. The one with the most reads his. He must justify his choice and, if challenged, be ready to use it in a sentence. Others in turn read until all have been heard and if necessary explained.

Dictate three recent words from other languages (from the above list or your own additions). Each player writes sentences using them. The group decides which are most effective.

Makaword

Each player is to make up three new words, not in the dictionary. He then writes a sentence for each word and must be ready to explain the meaning he has given it. Group decides which new words are most useful. Here are a few I have just made up: *omnibent, phoniac, hurlidub, brautop, plendor.* Their meanings:

Omnibent, of course, means ready to go along with anything.
A *phoniac* is a person (your sister?) who is never off the 'phone.
A *hurlidub* is a person who tries to brush everyone off.
A *brautop* is a sort of would-be highbrow, who puts on know-it-all airs.
Plendor is the name given to a man's long hair. He is *plendorous.*

This time make up the most pleasant-sounding words you can. Use in sentences, and explain. The group decides which are most attractive. Such as *claudilune, prestigate, magnamost, allasuperba, musiclimb.*

A *claudilune* is one who never gets to bed before dawn.
To be *prestigate* is to be wise beyond one's years.
The *magnamost* is the most popular at the pad.
Allasuperba means the prettiest girl in town.
A *musiclimb* is a hi-fi expert.

Let us look around to see what new words our language could use. We have the descriptive *picturesque,* but no word like *literesque,* for the field of literature. Perhaps it would sound too much like *litter,* of which indeed we have too much!

We have no one word for all varieties of physicians and surgeons. We did have the good word *leech,* but a *bloodsucker* took it away. A doctor may be a dentist, a lawyer, a professor, a philanthropist.

We also need:

1. A pronoun meaning a person of either sex, combining he and she, or him and her.

2. A possessive pronoun for things, like *whose* for persons. *Of which* is often clumsy.

3. The opposite of a liar. You may have noticed that in Chapter 5, speaking of the Cretans, I used the word *truther.* Perhaps some day dictionaries will admit it. (It is interesting to

note that we may accuse someone of telling *a* lie, but urge him to tell *the* truth, as though lies were many, but the truth is invariable and one.)

4. The mean between extremes. We can say *cold, cool, tepid, lukewarm, hot*—but what word expresses the mean between hard and soft, short and long, near and far? We can say *middle* or *middling,* but that is *piddling;* they fit too broadly, and leave us in the middle of nowhere.

5. Note that *soft* itself has to do double duty: *hard, soft,* but also *loud, soft.* The same for *short* and *long,* which refer not only to distance but to speech: short vowels and long vowels. And when someone exclaims: "That's hard!" does he mean the opposite of *soft* or of *easy?*

Another such double-duty word is *light,* which must serve as the opposite of *dark* and also of *heavy.*

When someone bids you, "Be still!" or "Be quiet!" does he desire absence of sound, or absence of motion? "Stop fidgeting!" or "Stop that noise!"?

Does *alight* refer to *getting off* or to a *scratched match?* Does a *match* mean something that gives a *light* or *one's equal* or an *exact correspondence* or a *game* or an *engagement?* Can't the language do better than this?

6. We speak of a *poet* but lack a good word for a *writer of prose.* A *proser* is a *dull bore.*

7. Some persons have a good *memory;* more have a good *forgettery*—which has its values too.

Some day, when your genius is prodding you, try to make up words for some of the gaps in our language. Pleasant-sounding, usable words. Words of one syllable may be effective. If you get some good ones, send them to me.

Occasionally, words have been invented in playfulness, even as deliberate nonsense. Shakespeare played this game too, as when he made up the speeches of Moth and Costard in *Love's Labour's Lost:*

> Moth: They have been at a feast of languages, and stolen the scraps.
> Costard: Oh! They have lived long on the alms-basket of words. I

marvel thy master hath not eaten thee for a word; for thou art not so
long by the head as honorificabilitudinitatibus; thou art easier swal-
lowed than a flap-dragon.

Nonsensations

Each player writes a paragraph, a little story or description.
Most of it should make sense, but every now and then he slips
in a word (one he makes up) to bewilder if not baffle the reader.
Allow about five minutes. Have at least three nonsense words
in the passage. Each player reads his paragraph aloud, and the
group decides which is the most amusing. Mark Twain, among
others, has done this in his books.

Other writers, instead of slipping a nonsense word into an
otherwise sensible discourse, build up a whole nonsense world.
Lewis Carroll begins his poem "Jabberwocky" with the lines:

> 'Twas brillig, and the slithy toves
> Did gyre and gimble in the wabe;
> All mimsy were the borogoves,
> And the mome raths outgrabe.

He explains some of these words as telescoped—two words
pressed together like the sections of a hand telescope. Thus the
word *slithy* squunches *lithe* and *slimy*. (*Squunch* telescopes
squeeze and *crunch*.) One telescoped word Carroll invented
that has come into the language is *chortle,* a pressing together
of *chuckle* and *snort*. Other such words grew into the language:
blotch from *blot* and *botch; clump* from *chunk* and *lump; flurry*
from *flutter* and *hurry; flush* from *flash* and *blush; knoll* from
knell and *toll; twirl* from *twist* and *whirl; slosh* from *slop* and
slush; splatter from *splash* and *spatter.*

The process still goes on. Many commercial terms are formed
by telescoping two ideas or words, as an automatic laundry is
called a *laundromat.* A man who drives his motorcar right to
the room where he is going to sleep is probably at a *motel.* If
he gets up late, and combines his first two meals, he eats *brunch.*
As he drives to the city, he hopes he will not find that mixture
of smoke and fog distressingly pressed into *smog.*

There are no doubt many other ideas for which two words can be effectively squeezed into one. When you have time to fill, try to think of some. If you get a good word, send it to me.

In 1914, Gelett Burgess wrote a "new dictionary of words you have always needed." Most of his suggestions are purely humorous or far-fetched, unusable words like *huzzlecoo, goigsome, orobaldity, jujasm, gollohix.* Burgess did, however, suggest the word *blurb,* which has become popular for what our literary grandfathers called a *puff:* a friend's or publisher's praise of a new book, now often printed on the book's jacket. Some credit Burgess with the coining of *bromide* to mean a trite remark, though this is probably a transfer from the chemical bromide, used as a sedative that made folks drowsy.

We are told that the word *quiz* was created on a wager, when a Dublin theater man bet that he could invent a word and make it popular overnight. He had *quiz* scrawled on walls and houses throughout the city. The next day the citizens *quizzed* one another as to what it was all about. You are permitted to be *quizzical* about this one; the Oxford English Dictionary says that the origin of *quiz* is "obscure." Eric Partridge suggests that the word was clipped from in*quis*itive.

Root 'Em Out

If you try to break up a word to see what it is made of, you first clear away any prefix or suffix. This leaves the stem, which is the same in various forms of the word. Within, but often the same as, the stem, is the root, the basic form that gives the core of meaning, in English and in whatever language the word came from. (Both our Germanic and our Latin words sprang from an earlier common word source, the Indo-European.) Prefixes are preempted by Chapter 9; suffixes will suffice in Chapter 12. Now let us look at roots. Here are some roots out of which English words have grown:

sens, sent—feel	leg, lect—choose, read	ag, ig, act—do, drive
cur, cour—run	seq, sec—cut, follow	flec, flex—bend
vers, vert—turn	ven(t)—come	pel, puls—push, drive
graph—write	plex, plic, ply—fold	sist, stan, stat—stand, place
fug—flee	grad, gress—step	tac, tang, ting—touch
cres—grow	duce, duct—lead	voc, voke—call

spir—breathe   clos, clude, clus—close   mob, mov, mot—move
vis, vid—see   spic, spec—look, appear   fac, fic, fy, fect—make
port—carry   tract, treat—pull, handle

Give players one root. Allow three minutes to write as many words as they can, using that root. Each in turn gives a sentence using one of his words, and must be ready to give the meaning. Player with the most correct words wins.

In three minutes, each player writes as many roots as he can. The one with the fewest roots reads his first, and gives two English words for each root. Others cancel roots as read, but give their English words, if they have different ones. Player with the next fewest roots reads his, and so on.

Give players three roots, or common endings. Allow three minutes to write as many words as they can make by adding prefixes. One with the most good words no one else has wins. For instance: *attain, contain, detain, abstain, entertain, obtain, pertain, curtain, sustain, retain, fountain, captain, mountain, sextain.*

Languages to Order

Scientists, practical men, and dreamers for several centuries have pondered the possibility of a universal language, which everyone some day might use in universal peace. Of the various artificial languages, Esperanto, presented to a largely indifferent world in 1887, has proved the most popular. There are printed books, radio programs, and annual conventions in Esperanto. It is limited, unfortunately, by being based on Indo-European roots, so the millions in Africa and Eastern Asia are left out in the cold. English itself is so widespread, however, that several forms of pidgin English have sprung up in the Far East for trade purposes; and in 1926 C. K. Ogden and I. A. Richards cut our language down to 850 words they call Basic English, which they offered as a *B*ritish *A*merican *S*cientific *I*nternational *C*ommercial means of communication. Winston Churchill and Franklin Roosevelt both spoke out for it, but the United Nations prefers simultaneous translation in four widespread natural tongues.

A couple of centuries ago, Jonathan Swift and Thomas Sheridan invented several languages for their own correspondence, and had lots of fun writing, say, in Latino-English. They used the same trick we boys used in my childhood with Francenglish: *Pas de leur aune que nous* might puzzle a Parisian, but a good reading would make it the sound American advice: "Paddle your own canoe."

We also had fun keeping outsiders guessing when we spoke to one another in Pig Latin. This has several patterns; the simplest is to put the first sound of a word at the end of the word, and follow it with the sound *kee*. "Umkee verokee ootkee eymkee ousehekee" is Pig Latin for "Come over to my house." After a little practice, sentences can be rolled off the tongue, and a few friends can talk it anywhere.

The grandson of Thomas Sheridan listened in Parliament one day to a man who climaxed his speech with a Greek quotation. Sheridan rose and said: "The learned member has apparently forgotten the rest of that passage, which contradicts the opening"—and he continued in what was Greek to Parliament for two more minutes. The "learned member" apologized for his slip; several of his colleagues told Sheridan they now recalled the passage, and congratulated him on his apt memory—and there was not one word of Greek in the resounding taradiddle he had uttered! I didn't believe that story until a classmate of mine confessed a similar episode. He delivered the Greek oration at our commencement, and midway forgot his lines. With an aplomb and fluency that have since helped make him one of our most distinguished trial lawyers, he went right ahead with meaningless but Greek-sounding syllables until his memory caught up to him. His Greek professor must have been startled; the rest of us were innocently unaware.

After all, as Swift undertook to demonstrate, Greek is merely an early outcropping of English. Look at just two examples, he said. We call a man who is by no means the life of the party *a killjoy*. Among the Greeks there was a warrior who was quick-tempered and unpredictable; he kept everybody nervous.

Naturally they called him *a kill-ease,* Achilles. And there was a great ruler of Macedon who liked his eggs roasted in the fire. Every morning, as the emperor stretched his arms on awakening, the bedside guard would call to the hall guard: "All eggs under the grate!" The hall guard passed the word, and down the corridors the call would echo to the waiting chef in the kitchen: "All eggs under the grate! All eggs under the grate!" Is it any wonder the emperor became known to history as Alexander the Great?

On a simpler level, a man asked a tailor: "Eumenides?" and the tailor responded: "Euripides?"

A little girl came over to a group of playing children and asked: "Can I Plato?" The Greeks had a word for it, and maybe the word became English.

9

BEGINNINGS: BEHEADINGS, FOLDERS, INITIAL WORDS, ACROSTICS COME FIRST

We are told in the Bible (John 1:1) that "in the beginning was the word." Let us look at the beginning of the word. Unless a word plunges at once to the root, it begins with a prefix. *Pre-* means *before;* something is fixed before that qualifies and alters the whole.

There are several games that can be played with prefixes, or indeed with any group of letters at the start of a word. Let's look at some.

Assign the same prefix to all players. In three minutes they write all the words they can, beginning with that prefix. The one with the most words reads first; others cancel words they have as they are read. Score five for each word no one else has. For other words, score the number in the group minus the number that have the word (if six are playing and two have a word: four points each). Deduct two for every wrong word.

Here are a few prefixes, with a few words for each. There are, of course, many more. Note that some prefixes change according to the letter that follows.

ab, abs (from)—absurd, abrupt, absolute, abase, abject, abduct, abhor, absent.

ad, ac, ap, as, at (to)—admit, assemble, approve, adjust, attack, admire.

com, col, con (together)—compare, collect, colleague, computer, combine, content, contract.

de (from, back)—defer, defy, detain, derail, depart, depopulate.

dif, dis (apart)—dismiss, disappear, disturb, differ.

en, em (in)—enlist, enslave, embody, employ, emphasize.

for (off, away, not)—forgive, forget, fortune, forfeit, forlorn.

fore (before)—forewarn, foretell, foreshadow, foresight.

per (through)—pertain, perhaps, persist, pervade.

pre (before)—prevail, prefer, predisposed, prejudice.

pro (ahead of, for)—prohibit, profane, produce, procession.

re (again)—regain, rebirth, rebound, reconsider.

Other groups of letters, not prefixes, are at the beginning of many words. We've already put the five vowels between *p* and *t*; let's try them as starters:

pat—patch, patent, paternal, patient, pathfinder.

pet—petal, petition, petrel, petroleum, petticoat.

pit—pitch, pitcher, pity, pith, pitfall.

pot—potato, potassium, potent, potable, potion.

put—putative, putrid, putt, putty, putrefy.

Now let's go to bat—batch, bath, bathysphere, baton, battalion.

Let's open a can—canal, canary, canasta, cancel, candy, candidate.

Or drive the car—caramel, carat, caravan, carbon, carouse.

Or sic the cat—cataclysm, catacomb, catapult, catch, cattle.

Try on the mini—minimum, miniature, minister, minimize.

Stick with the pin—pinafore, pincers, pinch, pink, pinnacle.

Look for the rat—ratify, ration, rattle, ratio, rather.

Master the man—mangle, mansion, mandolin, manicure.

Glance at the gal—galaxy, gallant, gallery, gallows, gallop.

Of course, you just give the players the letters of the beginning, and three minutes to write all they can. Later, any dictionary will show all they've missed.

Tell which beginning you are using. Then for each word give a clue and the number of letters. First finished, or the one with the most in three minutes, wins. Here are two sets of clues and number of letters:

A. *man-*
1. food from heaven, 5
2. written by hand, 10
3. opening to sewer, 7
4. lots, 4
5. chase for a fugitive, 7
6. violent madness, 5
7. large house, 7
8. Eastern fruit, 5
9. virility, 7
10. nail treatment, 8

B. *pro-*
1. plan of action, 7
2. likely, 8
3. dig into, 5
4. question to solve, 7
5. continue, 7
6. forbid, 8
7. university teacher, 9
8. utter, 9
9. seer, 7
10. suggest, 7 (61)

If you want to try more of these on your friends, turn to the pages in the dictionary with the beginning you choose, and find the fun of making up clues yourself.

Here are some sentences. Dictate one number at a time. Do not tell what the prefix is. The number of dashes shows the number of letters in the word. All blanks under a number have the same prefix beginning. The first player to fill all blanks correctly wins.

1. John had to _ _ _ _ _ that he _ _ _ _ _ _ _ the _ _ _ _ _ _ fellow, but was _ _ _ _ _ _ _ against giving his _ _ _ _ _ _ _. "If he knows where I live," John _ _ _ _ _, "he may seek to gain _ _ _ _ _ _ _ _ _ and take _ _ _ _ _ _ _ _ of me."

2. The _ _ _ _ _ _ _ are good musicians, no doubt; but I _ _ _ you not to _ _ _ _ _ _ _ _ / _ _ _ _ _ _ _ _ _ / _ _ _ _ _ _ _ he is not a modern. I _ _ _ _ _ _ _ that the _ _ _ _ things in life are _ _ _ _ _ _ _ _ _ and _ _ _ _ _ _ _, and they should _ _ _ _ _ _ to everybody.

3. _ _ _ _ _ _ _ it would be better to _ _ _ _ _ _ me to drive away the _ _ _ _ _ _ behind the column; he _ _ _ _ _ _ _ _ in _ _ _ _ _ _ _ out. . . . She has a most _ _ _ _ _ _ _ _ _ _ _ / _ _ _ _ _ _ _ _ _ _ _ and can get you to _ _ _ _ _ _ _ in any way she wants.

4. Frank could not _ _ _ _ _ _ _ himself, but showed his _ _ _ _ _ _ _ _ for the man who had broken the _ _ _ _ _ _ _ _ to build Frank's new house. . . . The _ _ _ _ _ _, which was escorted by three destroyers, bore a _ _ _ _ _ _ _ _ _ _ _ of foodstuffs; they tried to _ _ _ _ _ _ _ the enemy by taking a roundabout course. When they were

_ _ _ _ _ _ _ _ into the harbor, they were _ _ _ _ _ _ _ _ _ _ _ _
by the _ _ _ _ _ _ general on their safe arrival.

5. He had _ _ _ _ _ _ _ _ not to _ _ _ _ _ _ _ _ with the
_ _ _ _ _ _ _ _ _ _ _ _ _, but there were so many _ _ _ _ _ _ _ _ by
_ _ _ _ _ _ _ _ _ parties that he had to order an _ _ _ _ _ _ _ /
_ _ _ _ the cause of the ambassador's death.

If the group is having trouble, after a minute tell the beginning for each set: 1. *ad-* 2. *be-* 3. *per-* 4. *con-* 5. *in-*. (62)

Folders

Several games can be played with a hidden beginning, leading
to an oddly mismated or amusing end. Each player is given a
sheet of paper. He writes, then folds the paper (fp). Papers are
exchanged (ex), and *without seeing what's already written* each
writes again. Exchange once more. Then each reads aloud
what's on the sheet he now has. The group decides which is
most amusing. The ones who wrote on the winning sheet play
the game once again, with each other.

Here are ten games of the Folders family, any of which
should help give an evening laughter. Everyone writes what is
printed in italics; directions or examples of possible plays are
in parentheses. Abbreviations are instructions, as indicated
above.

1. *I want to get* (a bucket of steam) fp, ex *so that* (I can tell Susan what
   I think of her).
2. *I am going to* (Philadelphia) (take the evening off) fp, ex *so that* (I
   can ask for a 100 percent raise in salary).
3. *Suppose* (England had defeated the colonies) (Benjamin Franklin
   had invented the radio) fp, ex *then* (Dutchmen would be swimming
   at Coney Island).
4. *Take* (put in any object, for example: my left foot) fp, ex *and* (tell
   what to do with it, for example: keep it overnight in the freezer).
5. *What is* (a cucumber) (my name)? fp, ex *It is* (halfway to a frozen
   apple tart).
6. *What is a new way to* (brush off my coat) (keep smiling for thirty
   minutes)? fp, ex *By* (motoring to Yonkers and diving into the
   river).
7. *When I* (turn my eyes on you) (go around the corner) fp, ex *I see*

(what the iceman went into the kitchen for) (how snails climb trees).

8. (Onions) *are like* (wild horses) fp, ex *because* (Frances thought the gypsy was stealing her new wig).

9. *You can* (spin daisies) fp, ex *if* (oranges are sold in the shoestore).

10. *You can be* (quicker) (laughed at) (President) fp, ex *if* (you stand in the corner for seventeen minutes) (Tom walks up Main Street in his undies, leading a white mule).

Beheadings

More words than computers have counted can lose their first letter and become another word. Thus *glove* becomes *love* and *spat, pat.*

1. Give an example. Allow three minutes for players to write as many words that can be beheaded as they can. (No word beginning with *t*.) Each reads his list and the one with the most correct words wins. Deduct two points for every wrong word. (63)

2. Play the same way; but this time, use only words beginning with *t*. (64)

3. Now try for a double execution. Some words can be rebeheaded (first letter removed; new first letter removed) and make a word both times. Thus *stone, tone, one.* Allow three minutes to write as many as you can. (65)

You may remember Professor Thompson, who pinned a note on his classroom door: "Professor Thompson will not meet his classes today." Passing by a little later, he noticed that someone had crossed off the first letter of *classes*. The professor crossed off the next letter, and went on.

The next three games are clue variations of the three above. The clue is a synonym of the word you are to find. In game A you cancel the first letter of the first word to obtain the second word. In game B the first words all begin with *t*, which you cancel to obtain the second word. In game C you cancel the first letter of the first word to obtain the second word and cancel the first letter of the second word to obtain the third word.

	First Word Clue	*Second Word Clue*
A	1. dirt	frost
	2. small slice	organ (gives bile)
	3. little	broad avenue
	4. mutilate	direct toward target
	5. range	handle well
	6. small soft cake	for eating ice cream
	7. shovel up	confine in small space
	8. of little importance	of little weight
	9. not quick	not high
	10. fasten tightly	gives light

B	1. slight thing	gun
	2. high card	rear end
	3. ability to do or say the right thing	perform
	4. mix up string	where two lines meet
	5. underground mushroom	mess up, annoy
	6. be in contact	exclamation of pain
	7. musical sound	single
	8. walk on	peruse
	9. betrayal of one's country	cause
	10. work to be done	inquire

	First Word Clue	*Second Word Clue*	*Third Word Clue*
C	1. frown angrily	monk's hood	"wise" bird
	2. floating aimlessly	meaning	split
	3. with open mouth	yawn	tailless monkey
	4. separately	portion	skill in creating
	5. rubbish	foolhardy	what's left after burning
	6. tiny seed	opening in the skin	raw mineral
	7. large sleigh	narrow shelf	rim
	8. trail	speed contest	top card
	9. tendency	tear apart	finish
	10. Go away!	mouse catcher	toward, by (66)

And of course you can make your own clues for any of the words listed at the back of the book for games 63, 64, or 65.

Give players the word *sparkling*. Tell them that, by beheading or making internal slices, but not changing the order of the letters, they can reduce it, one letter at a time, until only one letter is left—and at every step down, it is still a good word. First finished wins. (67)

Initial Words

A number of words, both commercial and general, have been made from the letters at the beginning of a word. Among well-known trade names are Socony (Standard Oil Company of New York) and Nabisco (National Biscuit Company). In other fields, the ladies have given us the Waves (Women Accepted for Volunteer Emergency Service) and their British cousins, the Wrens (Women's Royal Naval Service). Social scorn (or envy) has stingingly labeled a descendant of early Americans a Wasp (White Anglo-Saxon Protestant). More general terms, in science, are radar (*ra*dio *d*etecting *a*nd *r*anging) and laser (*l*ight *a*mplification by *s*timulated *e*mission of *r*adiation).

Take names of well-known persons. Use their initials as the first letters of words that in some way describe the person. Players write down the words, then try to guess the person. First to get them all wins. Here are a few, for a starter:

1. Writer Supreme
2. War Commander
3. First Democrat Rere-elected
4. First Nurse
5. Baseball Royalty
6. Captivating Comic
7. Arranged Liberation
8. Ambitious Horror
9. After Euclid
10. Popular Painter
11. Mighty Threatening Thunderer
12. Noted Astronaut (68)

You may be able to make some initial words with the names of your friends, to use at a party.

The practice of initial writing is far from new. And at times it was a serious matter, as for the early Christians, who wanted to recognize one another but might be killed (by hungry lions in the arena) if recognized by the pagan Romans. One sign they used, as a sort of password, was a fish. For the letters of the Greek word for fish, *i–ch–th–y–s,* are the first letters of the Greek words meaning *Jesus Christ, God's Son, Saviour.*

Initial Clues. Write the letters of a friend's name down the paper. Next to each letter, write a word beginning with that letter. Make up a clue for each word. Give players the clue, and the number of letters in each word. You can do this with one friend, or prepare it in advance for all your friends at a party. Suppose you have a friend named Charles.

Name	Word	Clue, Number of Letters
C	candy	sweet to eat, 5
H	hungry	ready to eat, 6
A	angry	ire roused, 5
R	ready	prepared, 5
L	lazy	slothful, 4
E	easy	not hard, 4
S	slippery	makes you slide, 8

When the players figure out the words, ask them what the first letters spell. You can make it harder by changing the order of the words. (To amuse myself, I selected words all ending in *y*; of course, you do not have to.) Let's try *John*:

J	just	fair, 4
O	over	on top of, 4
H	hurrying	speeding, 8
N	never	at no time, 5

And one for a young lady:

F	funny	comical, 5
L	lovely	adorable, 6
O	open	not closed, 4
R	remember	keep in mind, 8
E	every	each one, 5
N	notice	observe, 6
C	careful	cautious, 7
E	elephant	trunked animal, 8

And now you're on your own.

Acrostics

A poem the lines of which begin with letters that spell a word, or are in alphabetical order, is called an acrostic. Acrostics have been popular in many languages for thousands of years. In the Bible, Psalm 119 is an alphabetical acrostic, with twenty-two stanzas for the twenty-two letters of the Hebrew alphabet. Each stanza has eight lines beginning with the same letter, from *aleph* and *beth* to *shin* and *taw*. Psalms 9, 10, 25, 34, 37, 111, 112, and 145 all have some sort of acrostical pattern. The prophecies of the Greek Erythraean Sybil were delivered in acrostics. The arguments (summaries) prefixed to the Latin plays of Plautus are acrostics. The

Arabs as well as the Hebrews enjoyed acrostics.

Elizabethan poems include numerous acrostics, especially with the name of the Queen. Lewis Carroll wrote several acrostics, among them the verses at the end of *Alice Through the Looking-Glass,* naming the girl for whom it was written. The American novelist James Branch Cabell, in his novel *Something About Eve*, has a sonnet the first letters of which spell "This is nonsense." Fortunately for his purpose, a sonnet has just fourteen lines.

Trickier patterns of the acrostic have occasionally been used. A mesostich (the *ch* is pronounced *k*) spells a word down the middle of the lines; the telestich, at the end. Sometimes one word goes down at the beginning, another down at the end; sometimes down in front and up in back, as in this quickly made-up example:

> Perhaps a poor rhyme, but it isn't a crime
> Laughing to venture when chances are slim,
> And always fall shy of a good alibi
> Yet not hesitate, whatever may wait.

Alliteration

You have seen an entire poem of alphabetical words, "The Battle of Belgrade," in Chapter 4. It illustrates a form of beginning less tricky than the acrostic and in smaller doses is much used by great poets for fine effects. It is what we call alliteration, the repetition of a sound at the beginning of words or accented syllables. "Apt alliteration's artful aid" can be noted in almost every poem ever written, and is frequent in literary prose as well.

Each player writes three sentences of brief description, or an episode, employing alliterative words. Do not pile them on; try to make them attractively add to the effectiveness of the writing. Each in turn reads his sentences, and the group decides which are most successful. The possibilities are virtually infinite. One might go like this:

The lovely lady looked out of her window across the wide expanse of stars. Somewhere a satellite was twinkling its tiny way through the heavens. A marvel of modern science, she reflected, making possible messages and pictures flashed wondrously around the world.

Some writers use alliteration more subtly, some more frequently, than others. Shakespeare and Keats are superb. Swinburne is excessive (as he recognized when he parodied his own work in "Heptalogia"). Tennyson, Coleridge, and Gray are somewhat subdued but noticeable. Gray's "Elegy Written in a Country Churchyard," long the most popular English poem, begins:

> The curfew tolls the knell of parting day,
> The lowing herd winds slowly o'er the lea,
> The plowman homeward plods his weary way,
> And leaves the world to darkness and to me.

Let's leave it at that.

10

MIDDLES: BURIED
(BUT NOT DEAD) WORDS;
RHOPES THAT BIND WORDS;
YOKINGS; CUT WORDS; KANGAROODLES;
TIEGRAMS; AND SUCH

When we speak of the golden *mean*, we do not *mean* what we *mean* when we say "Don't be *mean*!" We mean the *middle way.* Now let us *weigh the middle.* (How mad'll you be if I muddle when I meddle with the middle?) Let's try to keep it clear.

Middle Take

Many words become another word if you remove the second letter. Take the *1* out of *slay* and it is *say*, an indication that barter is better than the bomb.

Allow three minutes to write as many such words as the players can. Most wins. I set down over two hundred in a rainy half hour. (69)

Figure out the words from the clues, which are synonyms of the desired words.

Word Clue	*Second-letter-out Clue*
1. whiten	sandy shore
2. taken along	purchased
3. doubter	poisonous

Word Clue	*Second-letter-out Clue*
4. bee-pricked	uttered to music
5. imbibed	cake into coffee
6. sink in the sea	soft feathers
7. pebbles and sand	chairman's tool
8. male deer	droop
9. shocking news	open shoe
10. solemn	donated
11. sibling	pester
12. horse house	dark fur (69)

So too an *ounce* comes *once,* an *auction* gives you *action,* and how strangely *friends* become *fiends!*

Going farther along, you can remove the third letter of hosts of words, leaving another word. So *farther* becomes *father, resign* changes to *reign.*

Players see how many such words they can write in three minutes. (70)

Here are some third-letter-out words, clued:

Word Clue	*Third-letter-out Clue*
1. precipitous	pace
2. high polish	disappear
3. send to	also write name
4. in the mind	common kind of element
5. beggary	for illness
6. hurry	strong dislike
7. on top of water	even, level
8. Scotch skirt	packed equipment
9. ash	apple drink
10. duplicate	bashful
11. washed	Scottish tribe
12. infant	dip in coastline
13. inexpensive	fellow
14. somber	big deer
15. where the legs join	big smile
16. annoying insect	be defeated
17. tree tar	horse holder
18. Christmas plant	Christmas day
19. useless plant	married
20. made	boxed
21. sleeping fancy	drink
22. lively spirit	vindictiveness
23. scolder	thrasher
24. remover of sin	shake, as with cold (70)

Journey still another letter along. By removing the fourth letter, many a word becomes another, as *shouts* grow formidable in *shots.*

Allow three minutes for players to write as many such words as they can. (71)

Here are some fourth-letter-out words, clued:

Word Clue	Fourth-letter-out Clue
1. wound-marked	frightened
2. diagram	casual talk
3. shaver	with less on
4. pretending	disgracing
5. interweave	thin-headed nail
6. scrubbed	made a point
7. bottle stopped	apple ready to bake
8. ewe having baby	crippling
9. interfere with	lion trainer
10. begun	declared
11. chin adornment	part of neck adornment
12. diamond measure	small wagon
13. a cluster	a dip in water
14. wild animal	defeat
15. seashore	worn over suit
16. slice	pains
17. bird sound	marker in games
18. fasten tight	applaud
19. few	Go away!
20. big sign	one hard to solve
21. whine	of the vegetable kingdom
22. leaving	peeling
23. in the head	partly ground husk
24. usually evil magic woman	together (71)

Middle Find

A fairly large number of words lie complete between the first and last letters of another word. Tucked into *stand* is *tan*; inside *scored* is *core*.

Allow three minutes for players to write as many such words as they can. (72)

Figure out the words from the clues. Drop the first and the last letter, to find the buried word.

Full Word Clue	Buried Word Clue
1. Scottish child	atmosphere
2. discharged	anger
3. snort	speed along
4. disgrace	cured pork

Full Word Clue	Buried Word Clue
5. backbone	sticker
6. great anger	obnoxious rodent
7. hirsute adornment	auditory organ
8. foreigner	falsehood (72)

Every omitted word in the following passage contains the letter group *put-*. Explain this, then dictate the passage, giving the number of letters in the missing words—the dashes show how many. First player to supply the missing words wins.

Because of his great _ _ _ _ _ _ _ _ _, the _ _ _ _ _ _ _ _ _ from the scientific society came to _ _ _ before him their _ _ _ _ _ _ _ regarding the new _ _ _ _ _ _ _ _. At first he told them that the _ _ _ _ _ _ _ _ advantage was imaginary; the machine could not be programmed that way. But he proved to be _ _ _ _ _ in their hands and ended by agreeing to make the necessary _ _ _ _ _ _ _ _ _ _ _ _ himself. (73)

Rhopes

The great Greek hero Hercules carried a club. It was thin at the handle, and gradually thickened toward the head. And its Greek name gives us the word *rhope*. Rhopes are words that grow a letter at a time, sentences in which each word is a letter (or a syllable) longer than the one before, or verses in which each line is a foot longer. The most familiar rhopalic poem is Richard Crashaw's "Wishes: To My Supposed Mistress," which begins:

> Whoe'er she be,
> That not impossible she
> That shall command my heart and me . . .

Explain the rhope. Since each step must be a word, you can start only with *a, o,* or *i.* Players see how long a rhope they can weave in three minutes. Here are some samples:

a,	at,	rat,	tear,	trade,	parted,	tapered,	repeated,	desperate	
a,	an,	ran,	rain,	train,	strain,	retains,	strainer,	restrains,	transpires
a,	an,	ran,	rain,	train,	rating,	granite,	integral,	faltering,	flattering
I,	it,	tie,	diet,	tired,	direct,	cordite,	doctrine,	reduction,	introduces,
	destruction								
I,	it,	hit,	with,	white,	wither,	whither,	herewith,	wherewith	
O,	or,	ore,	over,	trove,	strove,	ventors,	investor,	inventors	
O,	on,	not,	tone,	stone,	honest,	thrones,	horniest,	thorniest	

Each player writes as long a sentence as he can, the first word of one letter, second word of two letters, third word of three letters, and so on. When a player has the longest word he can reach rhopalically, he may:

(a) Make the next word of one letter, and go up again. He may do this only once.

(b) Start counting down again, making each word one letter less.

(c) Stop. Or end with a one-letter word.

Group decides which is cleverest. Here is a possibility:

> I am not here every single morning; moreover, yesterday unexpected unwished-for catastrophic circumstances, unalteringly interfering, superseded initially hoped-for fragile dreams; alone down low am I.

Players have three minutes to write a rhopalic sentence. Same rules as for the previous game—except that, this time, the rhope grows not by letters but by syllables. For instance: Laugh, lunkhead, lumbering loquaciously, overconfident, unintelligibly overvociferating supersequipedalian bunk!

See how far players can go in a letter rhope without any change in the order of the letters. This time it is not necessary to start with one letter. For example: *but, butt, butte, butter, butters* (angry goats). *A, at, ate, late* can carry you through four more words. (74)

Reversing a rhope, you have an anarhope. Give players a word; they are to make words by dropping one letter at a time (rearranging the others if necessary) until they reach one letter. You can, of course, use any of the final words in the rhopes on page 117. Or try *flotsam, spaniels, cheaters, chosen, drowned, sprouted.* (74)

One rhopalic series has become a classic. Fill in the blanks; the director of a cemetery is speaking:

_ don't like _ _, said the man in the black _ _ _. It is true that

the _ _ _ _ is impressive, but when we _ _ _ _ _ a man, we
_ _ _ _ _ _ a _ _ _ _ _ _ _ identity. There will be a _ _ _ _ _ _ _ _
against _ _ _ _ _ _ _ _ _ when the _ _ _ _ _ _ _ _ _ of this is
recognized. (74)

There is an almost rhopalic summary of many a story: *he,
her, hero, heroine.*

Cut Words

Many words can be cut amidship, becoming two words. A
neat sudden appearance is from *nowhere* to *now here.*

Explain cut words, with an example. Players cut as many
words as they can in three minutes. Most wins. (75)

Cut the following by following the clue:

Whole Word Clue	First Part Clue	Second Part Clue
1. musical instrument	sack	tube
2. seaside roadway	plank	stroll
3. floating	water sign	tiny insect
4. depict	harbor	shaft of light
5. fool	monk's head covering	flick of the eye
6. fate	in favor of	melody
7. outspoken	out	correct
8. for baggage	payment not in cash	space
9. held up	route	put down
10. untouched	inside	gracious conduct
11. severely	estimator	partner in fight
12. shorten	mongrel	wagging end (75)

(a) What word of seven letters, without changing the letter
order, can be cut into ten other words?

(b) What odd number, beheaded, becomes even; curtailed,
becomes twilight and the mother of men?

(c) What word of six letters contains five pronouns, their
letters in order? (76)

There will be more of these cut words in Chapter 12.

Fill 'Em

In three minutes, players write as many words as they can, beginning with *r* and ending with *d* or *de.*

Try, another time, beginning with *c* and ending with *d* or *de.* Also *br* and *d.* And *h* and *d* or *de.* The one with the most letters wins. Thus *cad* and *code* together score less than *cavalcade; rode* and *record* together score less than *rodomontade.*

Ingrams

Many a word, if you tuck in a letter, becomes another word. Thus *sew + t = stew; trust + h = thrust.*

Players write as many Ingrams as they can in three minutes. Write them as in the sample: *clam + i = claim.* Most wins.

Clued Ingrams. Make five boxes down a sheet of paper. Two clues are given: to the first word, and to the word with the added letter. When you solve them, write them so that the added letter is in the box. For good measure, the boxed letters are an anagram of another word. First to get the boxed word wins. Here's one worked out, then three for you to try:

Clue to First Word	Added Letter	Clue to Second Word
bank it	s [h] ave	cut the hairs off
front of your head	fa [r] ce	slapstick comedy
large lump	[a] mass	collect
belonging to him	[t] his	the one here
cautious	w [e] ary	very tired

Anagram clue: pumping organ (heart)

1.

taps		trousers
no difficulty		rub out
pushed in		indicated
circling		boat on shore
egg layer		at what time

Anagram clue: full size

2.

crippled		accuse
place for money		empty
professional cook		head of the tribe
quite stout		so it is
big bag		hearty kiss

Anagram clue: go up

Clue to First Word	Added Letter	Clue to Second Word
3.		
school group		holds tight
harbor		sky
angry color		peruse
open shoe		shameful story
clock sound		solid

Anagram clue: inexpensive (77)

There are hosts of ingrams; here are just a few more: *bran+ d= brand; rain+ b= brain; bran+ i= brain; god+ a= goad; gnarled+ e= enlarged; ramble+ b= bramble; edit+ r= tried; eat+ l= late; eater+ h= heater; heater+ t= theater; one+ t= tone; tone+ s= stone; stone+ h= honest; honest+ r= hornets; taste+ l= latest; sleep+ a= please; part+ s= strap; glare+ r= larger; cornet+ o= coronet; hornet+ s= thrones; rifle+ t= filter; filter+ r= trifler.*

Tiegrams

Akin to the ingrams are the Tiegrams, two words that become one word when you tuck a letter between them.

Players write as many tiegrams as they can in three minutes. Write as in this sample: *fair+ y+ land.*

Follow the tiegram clues. Write on the appropriate side of the column the words you find. Put in the box the letter that ties them into one word. Letters in the box are an anagram; first to get the anagram word wins. Here is a sample, then three to try.

First Word Clue	Tie Letter	Second Word Clue
rooster	cock [t] ail	be sick
to write with	pen [i] tent	to sleep in outdoors
is able	can [n] on	not off
to see with	eye [g] lass	girl
be aware	know [l] edge	brink

Anagram clue: shine (glint)

1.		
thing flat and round		ready, . . . , fire!
what men wage		to live in
the present		twenty-four hours each
rear		circular
contradict		competent

Anagram clue: chairman's tool

First Word Clue	Tie Letter	Second Word Clue
2.		
not near		ground around house
heavy wire		male sheep
fine creation		be constricted in throat
male cow		cheap metal
penny		war partner

Anagram clue: dirt

3.		
mild drink		let fall
wound mark		black bird
her		article
juice		engage
weapon		of high temperature

Anagram clue: heavy lance (78)

Want some more? Set them up yourself: *bet+ o+ ken; gun+ b+ oat; deer+ s+ kin; tread+ m+ ill; never+ m+ ore; rain+ c+ oat; fool+ s+ cap; step+ m+ other; sin+ g+ song; hand+ i + work; forge+ t+ fully; ever+ y+ body; car+ o+ using; yell+ o+ wish; air+ e+ dale; torn+ a+ does; ear+ s+ hot; imp+ o+ sing; man+ s+ ion; convent+ i+ on.*

Steps

Take a pair of letters across a series of five-letter words, so that the pair makes the first two letters of the first word, the second and third letters of the second word, the third and fourth letters of the third word, and the fourth and fifth letters of the fourth word. Split the pair, to be first and last letters of the fifth word. Like this, with *te:*

> teams
>
> steal
>
> rated
>
> write
>
> twice

See whether players can make up a series of steps.

Figure out a few. Here are the letters and clues (but not in the right order).

A. *st*: flower
    social class in India
    topmost point
    clever
    one of our fifty

B. *de*: skillful
    retard
    loafer
    poisonous snake
    edge of knife

C. *re*: gaze at
    idea in sleep
    give in return
    wash soap out
    central parts (79)

Marsupials

Strange as it may seem, there are oodles of "kangaroodles," or marsupial words, in English. Marsupials, of which the kangaroo is the best known, are animals that carry their little ones in a pouch. A marsupial word is one that has within it (with the letters in their correct order) a littler word of the same sense family—a synonym. Thus *salvage* contains *save*.

In the following words, each dash represents a letter of the smaller synonym. Dictate six at a time. Players write the words with the blanks, then try to fill in the blanks. The first to finish wins. Work for one minute without clues; then dictate clues (given below) for the six you're working on.

1. -n-o--nt	13. --p---l-ion	25. -ont-i-er
2. --ce-se-	14. s-r-g-le	26. enco--a--
3. -eg--at-	15. se---a-e	27. --te--
4. ---pi-e	16. ---ke-	28. e---u---
5. pe----u-at-	17. -----u-ion	29. ---io---
6. ca-ac----	18. ---isfi--	30. --mpa--
7. --scu-in-	19. --s---ry	31. --li-er---
8. ex-st-	20. ---ad-	32. pro-ec-t-
9. --t---	21. ob--rv-	33. ---there-
10. pe---eter	22. -abr--a----	34. tran-gress-o-
11. --r-ail	23. -ppro-ria-e	35. -----v-s--
12. i-lum-na-ed	24. rec--n-	36. ---ch--

Clues:

1. lazy	13. scamp	25. holder
2. defunct	14. tussle	26. prod on
3. control	15. divide	27. final, most recent
4. temporary repose	16. selling place	28. clear out
5. walk about	17. uprising	29. fastened firmly
6. burial places	18. had enough	30. violent behavior
7. the "stronger sex"	19. inn	31. consider carefully
8. has being	20. the front	32. go to law against
9. circular	21. notice	33. slipped along
10. border	22. something made up	34. violation of rule
11. shorten	23. suitable	35. boss
12. lighted	24. rest down	36. is the same as

Now that you've found these, here are a few more, to see how easy it is once you've got the hang of it:

37. s---v--	41. -ci---	45. ----icad--
38. -l--	42. con--m--a---	46. -xa-t-----
39. dest--ct-o-	43. j--ct---	47. -na--mi--
40. ---tur--	44. ----ial--	48. -----em-n---

Clues:

37. attempts	41. descendants	45. blocked
38. hint	42. infected	46. rapture
39. devastation	43. a joining together	47. oneness
40. attitudes	44. to some degree	48. finished, filled (80)

Buried Words

Between words still other connections may be fashioned. Words can be so placed in a sentence that the end of one word and the beginning of the next make a third word. This sounds rather tricky, but it's not really hard. Let's try with the word *trick*. Obviously, not many words end with *tr;* so we can try to end with *t*. Also, *tric* suggests *electric*. So here we go: Don't le*t rick*ety wagons keep you from the hayride, Justin. He got an elec*tric k*eyboard to control the lighting in his new theater. And there you have it. If you need an unusual word for your burial ground, put in another unusual word as a decoy. That's why I added *Justin,* just in case. Here are some buried fruits. Player that first finds them all should have his choice, to eat:

1. Their mishap pleased none but the doctor who was called to tend them.
2. He tried in vain to end a tension that had grown between them.
3. A little money goes a long way in some foreign lands.
4. If I get my hands on you, you'll never forget it!
5. I hope a charmer like you will come my way often, Eunice.
6. What a big rap every act got from the crusty critic! Wow!
7. The trained ape arranges blocks in piles, and eats with a knife and fork.
8. Once upon a time buffalo ran generally over our western plains. (81)

Now enjoy the fruits of your labor.

11

BOTH WAYS:
REVERSIBLES, TWIN ENDS;
PALINDROMES, AND ROAMERS;
DOUBLE CROSSES AND SQUARES

Reversibles

"We look before and after," the poet says. Here let us be content to look fore and aft. At the same word. Some words have the peculiar habit of changing themselves into other words if read backwards. Try this with *part,* and you fall into a *trap.* Set a trap for your friends.

Explain Reversibles. Then give clues for some. Here are a clued few to start with. Dictate six at a time.

Forward Clue	*Backward Clue*
1. guardian	make the picture over
2. in the sky	rodents
3. give forth	can't be hurried
4. midway in tennis	half a score
5. entrance	crucifix
6. pesky winged insect	strong fresh flavor
7. emphasized	for the last course
8. pace	pampered creatures
9. prepare for publication	oceanic up and down
10. scold	truth violator
11. crash into	spoil
12. disprove	thick root vegetable (82)

Here are a few more reversibles, for your dalliance:

keel	smart	evil	gulf	yard
buns	nuts	spin	sloop	doom
not	spoons	new	gnar	nap
diaper	tram	stops	span	nut

A few names allow a similar turnabout. Thus you may say to the poet T. S. Eliot: "Thou *toilest.*" Shaw—the *sh* being one unit of sound—becomes wash; and by the same token the writer of these words, though one would hardly call him a puppy, becomes *yelpish.* See whether some names you know are reversible.

Twin Ends

There is another group of words which begin and end with the same set of letters (two or more). *Sense* has *se* at both ends. *Testate* has *te;* so has *terminate.*

Fill in the following. Each dash represents a letter, the same at both ends. Give players six at a time; score five for any correct after one minute. Then give the clues. Now score, for each word, one plus the number of those that do not have it. Highest score wins.

1. --iment--	5. --avab--	9. --capad--
2. ---row---	6. ---anglem---	10. --ellfi--
3. ---to---	7. --eepi--	11. --ifi--
4. ---icem---	8. --otogra--	12. ---est---

Clues:

1. regarding your food	5. can be abandoned	9. wild pranks
2. painful toenails	6. state of being mixed up	10. crustaceans
3. gives back	7. bashful	11. informed, uplifted
4. allure	8. camera shot	12. taking into the stomach (83)

Players write as many twin ends as they can in three minutes. Here are a few more:

insulin	enliven	escapes	teammate
esquires	deride	edited	temperate
estates	allowal	entrancement	verve
alembical	orator	headache	educated
chaffinch	desuetude	entertainment	

Finding more is not hard. A simple way is to think of common endings—*es, ed, est, ing*—and then think of (or hunt in the dictionary) words beginning with these letters that can use the ending. Easiest is *st,* which forms the superlative of forty adjectives, from *stablest* to *sturdiest.* The "thou" form of the verb, as "thou staggerest," gives more. Try also the poetic form: "He thriveth that obeys when the Lord threateneth." Among these, you can find enough twin ends to keep your friends guessing.

Palindromes

Some words are identical twins, the same backwards and forwards, like *peep* and *sees.* Words, phrases, and sentences that read the same both ways are called Palindromes. They are sometimes called sotadics, as invented by Sotades in the third century B.C. Ptolemy II Philadelphus had Sotades sealed in a leaden chest and dropped into the sea, but not because of his palindromes. A good Greek Christian palindrome—found in several churches supposedly including Notre Dame in Paris, but I didn't see it there—is the sanitary and pious counsel: *Nipson anomemata me monan opsin.* "Wash your sins, not just your face." (Note that *ps* is one letter in Greek.)

A clever Latin palindrome is the lawyer's bid for clients: *Si nummi immunis.* "Pay me your fee and you go scot-free." One of Queen Elizabeth's ladies-in-waiting—they were always getting into trouble with the hotheaded redheaded Queen—on being sent from court took as her motto the neat Latin palindrome *ablata at alba*—"banished but blameless."

Many palindromic sentences have been devised. When Daniel was being thrust into the lions' den, his friends remarked: "Poor Dan is in a droop." If you are attacking a general evil, "name no one man." A Victorian aesthete, dismayed at the rapid growth of the Industrial Age, exclaimed: "No, it is opposed; art sees trade's opposition!" The chimes on election day ring: "Rise to vote, sir!" Very neat is the palindrome dedicated to the engineer George Washington Goethals: "A man, a plan, a canal—Panama!"

Perhaps the best-known palindromic sentence gives the gloomy thought of the imprisoned Napoleon: "Able was I ere I saw Elba." This is so familiar that variations have developed, as in a *New Yorker* magazine piece by Roger Angell, in 1969.

Picture a refugee from Cuba: "A dum reb was I ere I saw Bermuda." Or a proud returning tourist: "Unremarkable was I ere I saw Elba, Kramer, nu?" Palindromedaries could go no farther.

However, there is something you can do about palindromes. Give examples: dud, nun, Otto, mum. Dictate clues (seven at a time) with number of letters:

1. more of the bright color, 6
2. made god, 7
3. allude, 5
4. flat, 5
5. add to, 3
6. 12 M, 4
7. firm belief, 5

8. that which restores, 7
9. little fellow, 3
10. 1/60 of a drachm, 5
11. act, 4
12. relating to a city, 5
13. one who takes a quick second look, 8
14. shut one's mouth, 3 (84)

Roamers

A beginning-and-end game that challenges your knowledge of geography can be played by two or more. It's an enjoyable pastime for a trip in a car. "I'm going to—" says the first player, adding any city, state, country, body of water, or other place in space that he may fancy. Second player repeats this, and continues: "And then to—" He must name a place that begins with the letter the first place ends with. Continue in this fashion, each repeating all that's been said before. Anyone forgetting a place in the chain, or unable to add an appropriate place, drops out. Survivor wins.

A game may begin like this:

> I'm going to California. I'm going to California, and then to Alaska . . . and then to the Antartic . . . and then to the Congo . . . and then to Oswego . . . and then to Ohio [there are at least a score beginning and ending with O] . . . and then to Outer Space . . . and then to the Erie Canal . . . and then to Lapland . . . and then . . .

Sometimes one just likes to meander along. Try it with three-letter words. Assign every player the same word to start. The last two letters are to be used as the first two letters of the next word. (Names may be used.) See how far you can roam in three minutes. Longest meander wins. For instance:

> bow-owe-wet-eta-tab-Abe-bee-eel-elm
>   bed-Eda-day-aye-yen-end

Another time, try meandering with four-letter words, last two letters repeated:

> soon-once-cede-dear-arse-sere-ream-amid-idle-lead-adze-zero-
> rope-peri (or pear, peon, peel, peep, peer, etc.)-rite-team-
> amen . . .

For either of these last two games you can set a harder rule: After listing as many words as you can, end with the word you started with. (Or set a definite goal: the tenth word must be the same as the first. First one to reach this wins.)

Make a chain of four-letter words. Each new word uses three letters of the word before (not necessarily in the same order) and one new letter. All start with the same word. The player with the most words in three minutes wins. For example:

> lose-does-dost-dust-bust-rust-rest-stir-sire-ripe-pear-peer-pier-
> pike-like-kail-mail-lame . . .

A tighter variation of the Roamer was devised by Lewis Carroll one Christmas as a present for two young ladies. He called it Doublets; I'd rather call it Crow Flight. Given two words of the same number of letters, move from one to the other by changing one letter at a time, always making a word. Thus from *head* to *tail* you can move: *head-heal-teal-tell-tall-tail.*

Here are some for you and your friends to try. One at a time is enough. The shortest Crow Flight wins. Try *pig* into *sty, ship* to *sail, sin* to *woe, hate* to *love, hand* to *foot, black* to *white, try* to *win, safe* to *home, less* to *more.* (85)

Such journeys have also been called Paragrams.

Another way for a group to play is to have one player give a word of four letters, the next give another four-letter word. Then all start to make a path from the first to the second word. Keep a record (1) of the time each player takes and (2) of the number of words each makes. Continue for four sets, or until every player has a chance to give the first word.

Score: Two points for each minute or fraction thereof, three points for each word in the path. Player with *fewest* points wins.

Thus if first player says *lead,* second player, *nuts,* two scores might be:

A: Three minutes. *lead-dead-deed-feed-fees-gees-gets-guts-nuts.* 33 points.

B: Four and a half minutes. *lead-leas-lets-nets-nuts.* 25 points. B wins.

For *star* to *bits:*

A: *star-soar-boar-boas-bias-bits.*

B: *star-sear-seas-sets-sits(bets)-bits.* Shortest time wins.

Double Cross

This game is simply made, and can be as easy or as hard as you wish. It is played with words having an odd number of letters. Let's try first with five. Make a cross, five boxes each way. Think of two five-letter words with the same middle letter, put that letter in the middle box, and give clues for the two words. For example:

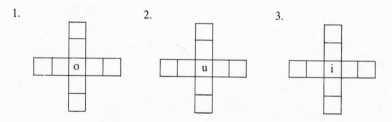

Clues: 1. makes garments, blossom; 2. believe, outside bread; 3. can't see, go up.

Other five-letter Double Crosses are *train-slate, bring-flint, punch-lunch, sight-might, charm-meant.*

Here are two seven-letter Double Crosses:

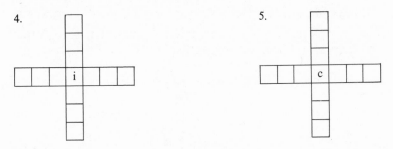

Clues: 4. credit, made ready; 5. business company, no harmony.

Other seven-letter Double Crosses are *rebound-immoral, fashion-highest, pretend-weather, contend-whether, brother-flatter, shudder-condone.*

Finally, here are two Double Crosses of nine letters:

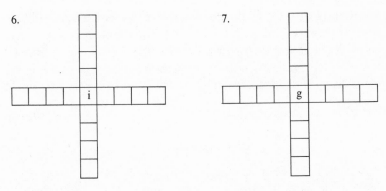

Clues: 6. trite remark, seasoning; 7. giving up a post, point out, assign. (86)

A few more nine-letter Double Crosses: *charities-multitude; happiness-compiling; dishonest-meteorite; skeptical-creatures.*

Four Cross

With the same shape as the Double Cross, this game may be called the Four Cross, because the middle letter does duty four ways. It is the last letter of a word from the top and of a word from the left; from the center, it is the first letter of a word going right and of a word going down. Give clues; four three-letter words in each cross. For example:

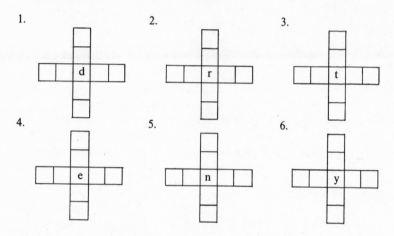

Clues start with the top word, and move clockwise. 1. naughty, put on, twenty-four hours, angry; 2. equal value, rodent, uncooked, spoil; 3. goes together, mild drink, heavy weight, floor cover; 4. falsify, finish, consume, buzzer; 5. examine, at present, short sleep, forbid; 6. remark, O.K., second person, attempt. (87)

Squares

Words have been arranged in many shapes: squares, diamonds, triangles, pyramids. A lot of energy, time, and patience have gone into their creation, the point being to arrange the letters so that the same words are spelled both across and down. Here are squares of three, four, and five letters.

U	S	E
S	U	E
E	E	L

L	A	N	E
A	R	E	A
N	E	A	R
E	A	R	S

W	A	S	T	E
A	C	T	O	R
S	T	O	N	E
T	O	N	I	C
E	R	E	C	T

They can be made with more letters, and several hundred have been concocted with nine letters, but these have to use unfamiliar forms, and names of faraway places. The English are not the only square dealers; Icelandic and Esperanto are among the languages of squares. Squares are exercises in ingenuity and wordplay. If you want to try your hand at the game, begin with three-letter squares; they are fairly easy.

One very old square had a secret meaning. It is scratched into the stone of a Roman wall in England. It was used as a magic charm for centuries. And it is not only a square but a palindrome; it reads the same forward and backward, up and down. Except for a name, its words

S	A	T	O	R
A	R	E	P	O
T	E	N	E	T
O	P	E	R	A
R	O	T	A	S

are good Latin; they seem to mean: "Arepo the sower holds the wheels to the work." But it's the secret sense that counts. The central cross, *tenet,* means *he holds (firm).* And all the letters can be rearranged to make an eleven-letter cross spelling *paternoster* down and across—with four letters over. These four are *A,O,A,O—alpha* and *omega,* "the beginning and the end," used in the Bible to describe Jesus Christ. So the square holds three Christian symbols: the Cross, the Lord's Prayer (Paternoster), and the alpha and omega. Thus the square was a holy sign, and it may—like the acrostic fish—have been used by the early Christians to identify themselves in times of persecution.

But you can play games with the squares. Draw a box of squares, and fill it.

Here are clues for some four-word (four-letter) squares:

1. bang; Tibetan monk; so be it; a large number.
2. expensive; otherwise; snakes; repose.
3. pillar; wind instrument; in a short time; portable shelter.
4. tear; lake and canal; fine; stag.
5. (The last three letters on one line are the first three on the next) moon movement; notion; darling; sound-catchers. (88)

And here are clues for some five-word (five-letter) squares:

1. outdoor game; time setter; yellowish earth; over again; tendency.
2. sections; around; way; teacher; severe.
3. sandy shore; harden; borer; belief; animal groups.
4. song; four-base hit; entertain; bird homes; lock of hair.
5. where rockets go; savage; representative; paddle boat; come in. (89)

Make a box of twenty-five squares. In order, write the letters of the alphabet, omitting *q*. Players write as many words as they can form from any combination of the letters, counting one space at a time in any direction (up, down, across, or slantwise). A letter may be used more than once in the same word. Words of two or more letters count.

In a similar box, arrange the twenty-five letters boustrophedon. That means first line left to right, next line right to left, and so on, alternating. (*Boustrophedon* is from a Greek word meaning "as the ox turns," in plowing a field.) This of course gives you quite a different arrangement of the letters. See how many words you can make now.

Regular

A	B	C	D	E
F	G	H	I	J
K	L	M	N	O
P	R	S	T	U
V	W	X	Y	Z

Boustrophedon

A	B	C	D	E
J	I	H	G	F
K	L	M	N	O
U	T	S	R	P
V	W	X	Y	Z

Twenty words make a good score for either pattern.
(90)

Players make a box of twenty-five squares. First player calls
out a letter. All enter it, in any square they wish. Second player
calls out a letter, which all enter. The same letter may be given
more than once. Continue until every square has a letter, trying
to arrange them so that you can spell words. Then allow three
minutes to write as many words as the player can find in his
box, counting one letter at a time, in any direction. Any letter
may be used more than once in a word. Score twenty points for
a six-letter word; ten points for a five-letter word; five for a
four-letter word; two for a three-letter word; one for a two-
letter word. The score for *pants* would be *pants* 10, *pa* 1, *pan*
2, *pant* 5, *an* 1, *ant* 2, *ants* 5. Total, 26. *Peep* would be a valid
word (not moving from the *e* until it's used twice). Winner
displays his arrangement of letters.

12

ENDS: TAILING, CURTAILING, AMPHISBAENAE, BULL'S-EYE, LASTON, AND FINALITEASE

"All's well that ends well." Shakespeare says so, so let us look at ends.

The most obvious ends are suffixes. Chapter 3 probes *-able* and *-ible*. The suffix *-er* can mean *more*, as in *stronger*, or *one who*, as in *worker*. In this case, it is active (one who does); the passive is *-ee: employee, trainee, trustee*. Psychiatrist Joost A. M. Meerloo in his journey *Along the Fourth Dimension* speaks of the changes in the sense of time that hypnosis can make in the hypnotizee. A teacher, of course, has too many pupils to call them the ugly-sounding *teachees*.

Over 150 *one who* words end in *-er;* but there are also words ending *-eer* and *-ier*. Thus one may be a *volunteer* to be a *mountaineer;* a *financier* in Venice may hire a *gondolier*. Some day you may get a job as *overseer* of a *cashier*. A *mutineer* or *racketeer* is likely to be less popular.

See how many *-eer* words you can write. The one with the most correct in three minutes wins. Then try the *-ier* words. They must refer to persons; avoid, for instance, *chandelier* and *veneer*.

Not far from the New York*er* lives the Boston*ian*. There are also the words *physician, vegetarian, Italian, simian*.

Diminutive suffixes include *-let,* as in *brooklet* and *cutlet,* and *-ling,* as in *duckling* and *darling.* Other common suffixes are *-ant, -ity, -ness, -ic, -al.* Another is *-ous,* which means *full of,* as in *suspicious, vicious, delicious.* But be careful: *meretricious* has nothing to do with *merit;* and *pious* means full of *pi-ety.*

One limited subdivision of this is the *-dous* family. Write all the words you can with the ending *-dous.* (91)

One of the largest families of words is that formed with the suffix *-ion* and its variants. I have counted 186 ending *-ration,* and the league of *-nations* is even larger.

In addition, there are at least a dozen ways of spelling the *-tion* sound. In three minutes write all you can. Here are clues: 1. avoid; 2. place; 3. force; 4. rendering; 5. pillow; 6. act of joining; 7. broadsword; 8. noon meal; 9. strong emotion; 10. sea; 11. one skilled in harmony; 12. citizen of the main Soviet. (92)

Tailing

Usually an *s* makes a verb third person: *he runs.* Or a noun plural: *many runs.* In some cases, however, it forms an entirely new word. Here are clues, before and after. Take five at a time. Find the word that, with *s* added, makes another word:

Word	*With* s *added*
1. troubles	gentle stroke
2. like	donkey
3. royal sons	their sister
4. heavy wires	without a taxi
5. steel slivers with eye	unnecessary
6. grips	without palm and fingers
7. evil giants	their wife
8. donkeys	estimate
9. belongs to him	sound of scorn
10. suppuration	kitty (93)

Amphisbaena

The amphisbaena, well known to the ancient Greeks, is a fabulous serpent with a head at each end. It now exists only in pictures and dreams. But if you've ever cut worms for bait, you've probably seen both ends try to wriggle away—the tail has a life of its own. We saw a few cut words in the last chapter; here we'll remove the tails of some more, and let them have a life of their own.

First, take away the last letter of *note*. You may think it's shorter, but it's *not*.

Explain the amphisbaena, or cut word, to the group. Give an example: *capsize* breaks into *cap* and *size*. (You have a big head; what is your *capsize*?)

Players write as many such words as they can in three minutes. Each reads his list; the one with most amphisbaenae wins.

Now try for some clued amphisbaenae. Four at a time:

	Full Word	*Head*	*Tail*
1.	drop straight down	fruit with flattish pit	encountered
2.	flower	vehicle	country
3.	sire	very stout	not him
4.	table towel	short sleep	relative
5.	litter of pigs	distant	things in line
6.	nasal cavity	wickedness	you and me
7.	slides along	narrow opening	she owns it
8.	completely	little one	associate in war
9.	for crisping bread	toward	star flower
10.	tame bird	hog	immeasurable time
11.	feeble cry	idle fancy	for each
12.	group of delegates	young lady	charged particle
13.	food expert	perish	red (hair)
14.	responsibility	supported by	we
15.	reverberating	scheme	fine fellow
16.	legally	established rule	completely (94)

Here is a batch of amphisbaenae, with a line marking the break: *mum/my, break/age, hum/bug, pot/ion, imp/unity, cur/rent, cate/gory, cart/ridge, don/key, asp/halt, disc/lose, do/or, dove/tail, don/or, me/at, ink/ling, ash/ore, leg/ally, pad/lock, par/take, pen/ally, pro/cession, onto/genesis, cap/-rice, his/tory, sod/den, par/don, is/sue, fan/fare, convent/ion, plum/age, car/at, mint/age, an/arch, rue/fully, rum/my.*

Make clues to any of these words, as you wish, and set your friends working. To give you any more would be doubly trite, or amphisbaenal.

The cut word can also come in a different form, a tied amphisbaena, using the middle letter twice, as the end of the first word and as the beginning of the second. Thus *rampage* gives *ramp, page*. Here are some to start you: mis*s*ing, vio*l*ate, mis*t*rust, arc*h*ives, how*l*ing, bal*l*ast, for*t*ies, car*p*et, cen*t*ime, wan*t*ons, pan*t*ies, pas*t*ime, duc*t*ile, par*t*ake, cas*t*ors, comfor*t*able, whis*k*ey, ma*n*or, pri*m*ate.

Here are some tied amphisbaenae, arranged in a crisscross, with clues. There will be twelve words. Each line will have two four-letter words, using the same center letter, and one seven-letter word, the whole line.

Draw a crisscross, as below, and find the words from the clues. Take one at a time.

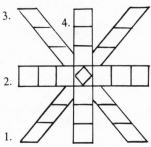

	Whole Word Clue	First Word Clue	Second Word Clue
A.			
1.	error	sort of fog	catch hold of
2.	destiny	military place	melody
3.	shorten	abrupt	rear end
4.	large dog	ship pole	quarrel
B.			
1.	sun satellites	scheme	meshworks
2.	full of thorns	make yarn	smeller
3.	projection on wall	cereal plant	pleasant
4.	Arab cloak	undergo combustion	intellect
C.			
1.	slender furry animals	market	half scores
2.	mild soap	hurl	slab of baked clay
3.	violent persons	sour, sharp	sailors
4.	military flights	kind	binds (95)

If the players are having trouble, give them the middle letter:
A. *t;* B. *n;* C. *t.*

Tied Ends. Explain the tied amphisbaena, with an example.
Players write as many as they can in three minutes. Here are
some more tied amphisbaenae: pas*s*port; hoc*k*ey; en*d*ive;
cas*h*ew; cros*s*word; dat*a*ble; di*g*est; per*i*odic; al*l*ot; extr*a*cted;
gover*n*or; pa*t*ent; por*t*rait; su*p*ine; pitc*h*er; brot*h*er; liquo*r*ice.

Bull's-Eye

In this game, the end is in the center, to which all the words
run. Have the players draw three concentric circles. Leave the
inner circle blank. Write the five vowels around the next space;
draw lines between them, extending to the outer edge. Divide
the outer segments in halves, making ten spaces.

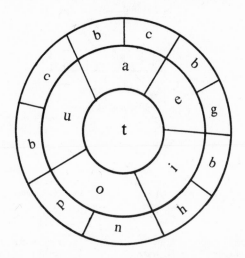

Now fill the spaces with three-letter words (two for each
vowel) all ending with the same center letter, as in the sample
above. First to get all ten wins.

Assign a middle letter. Good ones are *b, d, g, m, n, p, r, t.*
First to get ten words wins.

Give clues for ten words; first to get them wins. Here are two sets of clues:

> A. 1. feline; 2. for baseball; 3. slice; 4. except; 5. acquire; 6. matched pieces; 7. strike; 8. illuminated; 9. fate; 10. nix.
> B. 1. cup; 2. cut tree; 3. give; 4. scrap of cloth; 5. dance; 6. pull; 7. heavy mist; 8. petition; 9. large; 10. limb.

If players are having trouble, give them the center letter: A. *t*; B. *g*. (96)

Breakage

Some words break into parts of a sentence, or make some sort of silly sense. Here are six, with clues in parentheses:

> 1. Asked to fix a tear in her husband's trousers, what did the newly-wed reply? (beggar)
> 2. Asked whether he had played truant, what did the rascal do? (hinted)
> 3. When told the smudge was a masterpiece, what did the critic exclaim? (thistlelike vegetable)
> 4. Seeing him in a chair as the electricity was turned on, what did she think? (in orbit)
> 5. The child denied it strongly, crying: —. (sign of decay)
> 6. The gray dress was becoming, as she sat at the dinner table. (make friends) (97)

And here are several that need no clues:

> You should get some fresh air; you look quite paleozoic.
> He was so tired he went to the bench and Saturday.
> Buy bonds with your money? Investiture self!
> Was she hungry? I should satiate!
> He searched for his wandering son near and fatherly.
> Can a fisherman, or a Spanish dancer, more effectively castanet?
> When he takes a stroll, he likes to variegate [vary a gait].
> I'm amazed at the maze in the big field of maize, Maisie!
> As I was walking down the street, I metaphysician who said he had metonomy friends.
> I always like to pursue a good book.

More of these at the end of the chapter.

Here are more words that can be broken to produce other meanings (perhaps for homonimbles; remember them?):

invests; accrues (a cruise); reckon (wreck on); anneal (an eel); redress; attack (a tack); addiction (way of speaking); jell? (did you call?); admiration (I've eaten); automat (on the floor of the car); lonesome (I'm broke); expose (former attitude); beautiful (she's had enough); sunrise (mother's call).

Laston

Here is a goodly gathering of ends for you to tack onto beginnings. For all of them, you can play in two ways:

Players write as many words as they can in three minutes. Both the sound and the spelling count. For example: *-ain. Captain, obtain, mane, feign* are all valid. Player with the most letters wins, so think of long words.

Make clues. Tell the ending; give the clues. The first to finish, or the one with most in three minutes, wins. For several endings, I give clues: If you are hungry, here are some rations. Guess the *-ration* that:

1. hopes	7. acts as umpire
2. gets ready	8. pictures
3. parts	9. counts
4. curses	10. keeps cold
5. gets overheated	11. turns and turns
6. takes charge	12. makes a speech (98)

If you're still hungry, here are a few more: *restoration, incarceration, consideration, laceration, aberration, acceleration, admiration, corporation, infiltration, cooperation, emigration.* And over one hundred more.

The *-nations* include: *carnation, nomination, imagination, animation, alienation, culmination, coronation, ruination, dam-*

nation, alternation, termination, destination, consternation, impersonation, condemnation, dissemination, domination, elimination, insubordination, discrimination, abomination, consternation, and still more than the United Nations. (There is one repetition in this list; also, one word that does not belong. Did you catch them? If not, go back and find them. Always read carefully!) (99)

Is it a warm day? Have some ice. The *-ice* that:

1. no one likes to take	7. is a short space of time
2. is cut from a loaf	8. is a scheme
3. is very greedy	9. comes again
4. is biased	10. are tossed
5. is yellow-eyed	11. is a seasoning
6. is a fabulous serpent	12. is a steep uprising (100)

Some other ices are *price, nice, vice, mice, paradise, thrice, entice, cowardice, suffice, sacrifice, splice, precise, gneiss.*

How about a voyage? Take the *-ship* that:

1. makes you the best	7. sails to fight
2. makes life tough	8. rules alone
3. brings you close to someone	9. woos
4. is forbidding	10. plays fairly
5. lets you vote	11. presides
6. makes you boss	12. is a good shot (101)

Also: *relationship, township, lordship, acquaintanceship, seamanship, horsemanship, workmanship, partnership, worship, fellowship.*

After that exercise, perhaps your bones begin to ache. Let's find the *-ake* that:

1. is a spread of water	7. abandons
2. bosses the duck	8. is false
3. bothers your brain	9. shakes up the land
4. gathers mown grass	10. is sweet to eat
5. slithers along	11. checks movement
6. is conscious	12. clasps hands (102)

Not to mention *take, make, pancake, sake, toothache, stake, shortcake, flake, mandrake, break, sweepstake, steak, bake, namesake.*

By now, you may need some aid. (Remember, either sound or spelling counts.) Let's get the *-ade* that:

1. is a tart refreshing drink
2. has been on the scales
3. is fancied in the ocean
4. is tapped as an honor
5. is fearful
6. is a beautiful stone
7. can be spread on your bread
8. keeps you in the dark
9. marks some temperature
10. is fired to win
11. is interwined
12. gets you to do something
13. is a worn-out horse (103)

As well as *dissuade, orangeade, arcade, barricade, ambuscade, blade, grade, blockade, brigade, maid, crusade, cascade, prayed, preyed, paid, sleighed, laid, frayed.*

Feeling well again? Want to make a date with Kate? The following clues are for words ending with either *-date* or *-cate*. Find the one that:

1. resigns
2. seeks office
3. is a wise guy
4. is a company
5. will explain
6. floods
7. clears of guilt
8. shows is no good
9. goes into disrepair
10. is frail
11. chews
12. is sober
13. oils
14. is in favor of
15. gets rid of
16. puts together
17. tames
18. tells falsehoods
19. copies
20. frightens
21. marks before
22. takes away
23. plunders
24. makes drunk (104)

Here are some more: *deprecate, postdate, suffocate, rusticate, implicate, excommunicate, adjudicate, mithridate, prognosticate, reciprocate, placate.*

Now perhaps it's time to get the gate. Open the *-gate*
that:

1. dominates	7. proclaims
2. censors	8. sails around
3. keeps apart	9. looks into
4. diversifies	10. punishes
5. gives verbal forms	11. questions
6. forms ridges	12. is the sum total (105)

Also *divagate, gait, propagate, abnegate, profligate, delegate.*

By yourself, or with a group, try to see how many four-letter
words you can make with the endings below. Take one at a
time. Before starting, write at the top of the paper the number
of words you think there will be. Score one for each word. With
a group, the player whose guess is closest—not to his own score
but to the largest number of words anyone has—gets four extra
points. Try any of these endings—and remember, four-letter
words only: *-ce, -de, -ke, -le, -me, -ne, -re, -se, -te, -nt, -rt, -st.*
(106)

Two books can carry you far along these paths. A *jaywalker*
is usually not a person we approve of, but J. Walker wrote a
rhyming dictionary—which the poet Byron used—in which the
words are arranged analphabetically, beginning with the *last*
letter of the word. Walker's first four words are *a, baa, caaba,*
and *indaba;* his last four are *frizz, buzz, humbuzz,* and
fuzz.
And the pleasantly named Clement Wood compiled a rhyming dictionary, arranged alphabetically by one-syllable, two-
syllable, and three-syllable rhymes. Wood's first rhyming group
shows the long *a* rhyme, from *affray* to *yea* and *yesterday;* his
last group is *fuzziness, muzziness, wuzziness.*

Finalitease

Give each player a piece of paper. He writes the beginning of a sentence. Papers are shuffled and exchanged, no one to get his own. Each player finishes the sentence he now has, as amusingly as he can. The papers are redistributed, and the sentences read aloud. The group decides which is cleverest. The two winners play again, with each other. Some possible beginnings are:

> The last time I thought about you . . .
> In the gathering darkness . . .
> On the table . . .
> Peeping out from under the sofa . . .
> Higher than a cloud . . .
> Halfway before last week . . .

Writers are advised to end with a punch. (A glutton is likely to end with a paunch.) Many a word can be twisted to a surprise ending by reading other words in its syllables. A man having a house built said to the architect: "Keep the attic cool, planetary" (plan it airy). Here is a horticulture of such final flowerings:

When the ship took the whiskey around the world as ballast, you can understand why the sailors had a balustrade. (When all the liquor was drunk, so were the sailors.)

She's already used up a dozen tablets; how long will this pilaster?

Hi, John! Let's go overture house!

Her glance implanted seeds of love in every heart, she had such fertilize.

There will be many waiting, Examiner; be sure you take no more students than you expectorate.

Tennis at ten every morning! Regularly to beatitude have to arrange well in advance.

When his boat went aground ten feet from the pier, the skipper growled: "I wondered which document."

They were playing for high stakes; how much was it he plankton the table?

At the county fair they came to the show sheep, and wondered whether the judge would panorama praise a ewe.

Mary kept everybody guessing; you could never tell what merriment.

Although the board was not festive, they were hungry, so the directorate.

The leader of the dissidents came into the meeting room and satisfaction on the right.

"One at a time!" the doctor said to the impatient patients. "We'll take each one intern."

Has he pains all over? Or does some special partake?

He thought he'd made a conquest when he cauterize.

He was reading the Bible and felt lonely, so he hunted for a palingenesis.

The medium said that she would go into a translator.

Shakespeare said there are tongues in trees, which can speak poems. Has a logarithm?

They brought the car dealer to the wreck, and asked: "Is this the truculent?"

Children, stop shouting! Don't get your paranoid.

Napoleon had many victories, because when they asked him: "Can you do that?" he thought of his native land and answered: "Corsican!"

The writer of these lines is a pungent:

Before I was born, the classical example of these devious ends was devised, of the bookkeeper who wore out the seat of his pants, notwith-standing.

There is also the old advice: If at first you don't succeed, triangles.

Now droll your own.

13

THE CHARADE BRIGADE:
GEORGE ELIOT, JANE EYRE,
AND THE QUEEN; PATSY'S
PIGTAIL IN A SCORE

Guessing games have always been a challenge, from the man at the fairgrounds who'll guess your weight—no charge if he's not within three pounds—to the fellow selecting the winning horse, or wondering whether to raise the bet at poker.

Of all the guessing word games, the greatest in popularity has been Charades. The novelist George Eliot described the game in the second line of a protesting jingle:

> The universe, I hold, is no charade,
> No acted pun, unriddled by a word.

The charade is a form of riddle, a word or phrase to be guessed. It is often broken into syllables, each of which, and then the word as a whole, is described in a more or less tricky fashion.

How far back charades were played we do not know, but a lady asked for some in a letter the year our country was born. And in the next year, 1777, they are mentioned, as part of a gentleman's accomplishments, in Sheridan's play *The School for Scandal*. In 1796 a man calling himself Peter Puzzlewell, Esq., published *A Choice Collection of Riddles, Charades, Etc.*

These early charades were usually written in rhyming jingles.

Try some of them. ("First," "second," etc., refer to syllables, or easily broken segments of the word.)

1. My first can never be wrong,
    My second's a fair field for cattle;
    My whole is the way you should fight
    If God is to favor your battle.

2. My first is a thing for the feet,
    My second is long at the head;
    My whole is under the sheet
    Before anyone is in bed.

3. My first is surely the ground,
    My second will quiver with fear;
    At my whole, if you are around,
    You may quickly disappear.

4. Through desert space, with fire and force
    My first his way pursued,
    His drink was water at its source,
    My second was his food.
    He had but little time to rest;
    Across the burning sand
    He bore my whole within his breast:
    It was the King's command.

5. My first is always in back,
    My second, you'll find, is just us;
    My whole is a sort of attack
    That makes a meddlesome fuss.

6. My first's a command to attend,
    My second is half of a score;
    My whole I've oft done to a friend,
    Who answers he'd welcome some more.

Here are a few in prose:

7. My first is nimble; my second innumerable; my whole is fatal.
8. My first is good in the laundry; my second's a little rock; my whole is a kind of chalk.
9. My first may clean the room; my second is excellent broiled; my whole runs around the track.

10. My first is a devilish rascal; my second will wander; while
    my whole gets better.
11. My first is out of his mind; my second comes before noon;
    my whole is the lady of the house.

Sometimes, with a tricky turn (like a devious crossword clue)
the whole is given in a lump challenge—with the number of
letters:

12. How hungry the fool was to gain! 5
13. In a fold one can grow. 8
14. A tress that keeps a door shut. 4
15. Banter not recommended for the elderly. 10 (107)

After a while, charades were not given in rhymes, but acted
out. This process began in France, with enacted proverbs. The
Duc de la Vallière described a comedy of proverbs in 1634. In
1654 King Louis XIV danced in a ballet of proverbs. For instance, "some swaggering scaramouches" danced against and
threatened some sober citizens, who turned and beat them off.
The audience had to guess the saying: "He that is afraid threat-
ens others." Eight volumes of *proverbes dramatiques* were published in 1781; half a century later, some were written by the
noted poet Alfred de Musset, which are still played by the
Comédie Française. Queen Catherine the Great of Russia during the eighteenth century used to make up dramatic proverbs
to be acted and guessed at her court. These are, of course, one
form of charades.

In England, by the mid-nineteenth century, enacted charades
were the rage. In the book *Jane Eyre* (1847) Jane watches the
fine folk play a game; in the same year, Thackeray has a game
in *Vanity Fair.* The book *Parlour Pastimes,* published in 1857,
gives the rules. But a whole century earlier, one form of charades was acted under the name Dumb Crambo.

In Dumb Crambo, no word is spoken. The company is divided into two teams. Team One hands Team Two a sheet of
paper on which a word is written. This word rhymes with the
word to be guessed. Team Two then proceeds to act out its

guesses. Suppose the written word given Team Two is *dough*.

Team Two enacts *enemy*. Team One shakes head; it's not *foe*. Team Two enacts *squat*. No, it's not *low*. And so on, until Team Two acts out *propelling a small boat*. Now Team One can speak; yes, it's *row*.

Now Team Two gives a word. The team that guesses soonest wins.

Of course, it's more fun to take words with not too many rhymes. *Row* is not really good, or *ate,* or *bat,* or *tread.* Neater rhymes might be:

> armor, farmer, charmer, disarmer, harmer
> kisses, hisses, misses, abysses, blisses
> denser, dispenser, fencer, censor, tensor
> fringe, hinge, binge, singe, twinge
> leveling, reveling, disheveling, bedeviling
> server, fervor, unnerver, swerver, deserver
> acquainted, painted, fainted, feinted, tainted, sainted

Several varieties of enacted charades have developed; any of them may be fun.

Solo: one against the group. One player gives the host a slip of folded paper, on which he has written a word, proverb, or title that he is going to enact. If he's going to act it as a unit, he holds up one finger; if by syllables or parts, as many fingers as parts he plans to perform.

He acts it out. First one to guess has the next turn. If no one guesses, he acts it again, in a different way. If the correct guesser has already had a turn, the next player on his right who hasn't had a turn gets his chance. When everyone has had a chance, the one who has guessed the most wins.

Good words to enact are *pacifist, cabbage, scandalize, straighten (stray), tendrils, infirm, handcuff, strawberries, pinafore, target.*

Puncharades. Again, one player against the group. Player gives the host a folded slip with a word on it—a word that has several meanings, such as *strike* (a clock *strikes,* workers *strike,* man at bat *strikes,* a fighter *strikes* his opponent, men at sea *strike* their sails, an actor *strikes* an attitude, an engineer *strikes* oil). The player enacts his word. Those who think they've guessed it raise hands. One is chosen; he enacts another meaning of the word. If he's right, first player tells the word. If he's wrong, score one against him, and another guesser tries. If no one can guess, the first player enacts it another way or acts another meaning. First one right scores one, and has his turn to enact a word. At the end, highest score wins.

Chapter 7 has a list of homonyms which can be used in this game, but words like *bear, hold,* and *match,* which have several meanings, can also be used.

Team Charades. Divide the company into two groups. One group goes out and decides upon a word. It comes in and acts the word, syllable by syllable or as a whole. If the other group cannot guess it, the word is acted again in a different way. When the word is guessed, the second group goes out to choose a word which it will act. Keep this up until refreshment time. At the end, the group that has guessed most quickly wins.

Before starting, players may agree that they'll enact not words but proverbs. Or they may decide to enact titles (books, plays, movies, etc.). *Gone with the Wind, Lohengrin, War and Peace*—many will suggest themselves.

The Game. Hollywood for a while took over a form of charades which it called The Game. This was played for enjoyment in the homes of the stars (or, more often, of their scriptwriters) and for profit on television. The company is divided into two groups, each choosing a captain. Team One gives the captain of Team Two a folded slip on which is written a word, a proverb, or a title. The captain passes it, unread, to a player on his team. This player must—without saying a word—enact the term so that his group can guess it. They guess as quickly as they can. Time is kept, but thirty seconds are added to their time for each wrong guess.

When his team has guessed correctly, the captain of Team Two passes a paper to his opponent, and the procedure is the same. While the actor cannot speak, certain gestures have become standard practice to speed the game along:

1. Hold up fingers to show how many words in the expression. Circle of middle finger and thumb: it will be acted as a whole. If it is to be divided, right hand chops back of left hand, once for each part to be separately enacted.
2. If his team is slow at guessing, the actor may wave his hands in front of his face, to show he's starting over, to act the word a different way.
3. For a bad guess, head shakes no. If the guess is "warm," actor motions with both hands toward himself: "Get closer!"
4. To show smaller size, hands move slowly together; for bigger, or farther away, hands move slowly apart.
5. Other gestures are natural:
   Pointing at man or woman to indicate sex.
   Hand extended to shake: friendship, meeting, etc.
   Hands joined in prayer: piety, Bible character or story, etc.
   Pointing at a similar object.
   Pointing at the floor means *here*.

The Game has slipped off television, but it is still actively played in many homes. We are told that it is a favorite game of Queen Elizabeth II of England, who often plays it with her houseguests. It's a good way to take guests' minds off the state of the world. Happy hunting of The Game!

Score

Quite another guessing game has long been popular. It used to be called Animal, Vegetable, or Mineral? because these are the first questions naturally asked. Once you could ask as many questions as you needed; now you are usually restricted to a score. Not the score of a game; not the score in a tree trunk; not the score that you owe; not the score the orchestra plays— but the score that is twenty. You have to guess in no more than Twenty Questions (a current name for the game).

One person leaves the room. The others decide on something the returning player must guess. The questions usually begin

"Is it . . . ?" Each person in the room, questioned in turn, may answer only yes or no.

You usually begin by asking if it's animal, vegetable, or mineral. If it's none of these, it's abstract. When the first player has guessed, another goes out, and a new thing is chosen to be guessed. The one who gets the right answer in the fewest questions wins. You'll be astonished how you can score in a score of questions.

If the game is new to the players, it's best to start with objects:

> page 97 of the third book on the second right-hand shelf
> Patsy's pigtail
> the person on the left of the one being questioned

You can go farther afield:

> Julius Caesar's first step after he crossed the Rubicon
> the soldiers whom Xerxes ordered to whip the waves
> a feather from the right wing of the Angel Gabriel
> the sprig of live leaves the dove brought back to Noah's ark

As the group grows more experienced, you may move on to things immeasurable:

> the day man discovers a cure for cancer
> the back door of eternity
> the astronauts' emotion as they first stepped upon the moon
> the anticipation of Doomsday in the devil's mind
> the paradox of infinity in a little room
> the joy of the player when he makes the right guess

As I write, the BBC in the year of 1971 is broadcasting as a weekly series the game of Animal, Vegetable, or Mineral? Play it, and find out your score.

14

SOUND: SPELLS,
HARMONIES, ECHOES,
AND TWISTERS

Sounds are tricky things. Some tongues have trouble with sounds. There are sounds in other languages—like the German *ch*, the French *r*, the Chinese slides—which are hard to pronounce for many people who speak only English. A Chinese may say "flied lice" when he means "fried rice," and a Japanese may pronounce the *l* as an *r*. I was startled once, in Tokyo, when a friendly Japanese wished me a "happy horriday."

We may overlook the fact that this very shift is buried in our own language. The French pronounce the word *colonel* with an *l* sound in the middle; we pronounce it as though it were the inside of a nut. One nickname of *Mary* is *Molly*. Henry V of England as a young man was Prince *Harry* or Prince *Hal*.

Such language shifts have been put to drastic use. The Bible (Judges 12: 4–6) tells how the Gileadites asked their enemies, the Ephraimites, to say "shibboleth." They could not, saying "sibboleth" instead—and forty-two thousand Ephraimites, thus identified, were slain. The word *shibboleth* has come into our language, meaning *password* or *test*.

In the same sound transfer, the Semites are the children of Shem. Arabic *salaam* is Hebrew *shalom*, both meaning *peace*. (There's an *h* of a difference! Perhaps that's why they find it so hard to agree on peace.)

We pronounce *phlegm flem* but *phlegmatic flegmatic*. The measure *drachm* is pronounced *dram,* but the coin *drachma* is pronounced *drakma*. *Schemer* begins with the *sk* sound, *schism,* with *s; schist,* with *sh*. *Schedule* is pronounced with *sk* in America, but *sh* in England. We may go *skiing* on snow-covered slopes in the United States, but in Europe they go *she-ing*. The German *Fisch* is one with the Scandinavian *fisk*.

In three minutes, players write as many words as they can, beginning with *ch* pronounced *k*. A good score is twenty; excellent, thirty.

Take three minutes more to write words beginning with *ch* pronounced *sh*. There should be quite as many. (108)

In *dumb* and *dumber, plumb* and *plumber* the *b* is silent. So also in *limb,* but in *limber* and *lumber* the *b* is pronounced. *Numb* is *m, number, mb*. But be careful. We speak of an odd or an even *number*. But there was a group of climbers on a Himalayan mountain, *numb* with cold. And how odd! Henry was even *number* than the rest! And this time, the *b* in *number* is silent.

Mnemonics, which means devices to help the memory, begins with the *n* sound. So do *pneumatic* and *pneumonia*. The *p* is also silent in words beginning with *psych* and in the *pt* forms *(ptarmigan, pterodactyl, ptomaine)*. The *c* is silent in *ctenoid*—which has no relation to teen-age. *The Random House Dictionary* lists ten words beginning *ct,* pronounced *t*.

Try *phth*. You find it in *naphtha, diphthong, diphtheria*. The *Oxford Shorter English Dictionary* lists four words beginning *phth*. According to this authority,

phthalic begins with the sound	*fth*
phthiriasis begins	*th*
phthisic begins	*t*
phthisis begins either	*th, t,* or *fth!*

"You pays your penny, and you takes their choice."

Write words showing as many different sounds of the combination *ough* as you can think of. (109)

Instead of one combination of letters representing several sounds, one sound may be represented by various combinations of letters.

Try only one of these at a time. Write words showing as many different spellings as you can for the following sounds:

$\bar{o}$ (fifteen is excellent)	$\bar{u}$ (twelve or more)	$\bar{e}$ (ten or more)
s (six or more)	sh (fifteen or more)	t (eight or more) (110)

What word of five letters can lose four and still have the same sound? Clue: Line up! (111)

A frequent change of sound is from the present to the past of what are called strong, or irregular, verbs. Thus *speak* becomes *spoke; break, broke; seek, sought. Work* may become either *worked* or *wrought;* but *wreak* becomes *wreaked; leak, leaked; stake, staked.* Writers have played upon these variations. There are verses that mock such words. One stanza runs:

> So they to each other were clinging, and clung,
> While Time his swift circuit was winging, and wung,
> And this was the thing he was bringing, and brung.
> (I suppose that the church chimes were dinging, and dung.)

Try to make your use of sound sound sound.

15

ARE YOU AVERSE TO VERSE?
RHYME HAS ITS UNREASON.
TRY THE HAIKU.

The Limerick

In 1817, three authors spent Christmas together. Wordsworth kept quoting from Virgil and from Milton. Keats listened. And Lamb kept breaking in with:

> Diddle diddle dumpling, my son John
> Went to bed with his britches on.
> One shoe off and one shoe on,
> Diddle diddle dumpling, my son John.

A little nonsense now and then is relished by the best of men. It's one of my frequencies, too.

Out of the nursery rhyme came the limerick. The special limerick form, used exclusively for humorous verse, was caught by Mother Goose long before Edward Lear made it popular:

> Hickory dickory dock
> The mouse ran up the clock.
> The clock struck one
> And down it run,
> Hickory dickory dock.

It wasn't actually called a limerick until 1898, ten years after Lear had died. Nobody knows how it got the name, but everybody knows the pattern:

> A smiling young lady from Niger
> Went out for a ride on a tiger;
> They came back from the ride
> With the lady inside
> And the smile on the face of the tiger.

> For beauty I am not a star,
> There are others more handsome by far,
> But my face I don't mind it
> Because I'm behind it;
> It's the fellow in front gets the jar!

> A remarkable fellow named Bright
> Achieved a speed faster than light;
> He went out one day
> In a relative way,
> And returned on the previous night.

Oliver Wendell Holmes combined the form with a pun on his minister friend Henry Ward Beecher:

> There once was an eloquent preacher
> Called a hen a most elegant creature.
> The hen, pleased at that,
> Laid an egg in his hat,
> And thus did the hen reward Beecher.

Writing limericks—or making them up during a car ride—is a game I have played many times. For a group, it may be more fun to have some first pairs of lines ready. Give the same pair to all the players to complete. The group decides which is the most amusing. Here are a few possible starters:

> A handsome young fellow from Spain
> Went out for a stroll in the rain . . .

> A man heard a roar in a ruin
> And wondered what trouble was brewin' . . .

Walking westward one Friday at dusk
I encountered an elephant's tusk . . .

A youth flying at speed supersonic
Overtook a strong yen for a tonic . . .

A youngster from old Gillicuddy
Accepted a bear as a buddy . . .

Other amusing rhymes to challenge limerickshaws—and you can play by giving only the first line—might start:

There was a young man from Malacca . . .
(or) named Tumblethree . . . Applevote . . . Hasselfry . . .

or as your fancy strays.

Once you have played this game, take the next step. Each player makes up the first two lines of a limerick. Exchange papers. Each completes the limerick he now has. The two whose combined limerick is judged the most amusing play again.

Limericks have never gone out of vogue. They've been written on all sorts of subjects with every conceivable variation—especially of the last line, which has been lengthened, shortened, written without rhyme, or otherwise twisted for unexpected humorous endings. Newspapers and commercial firms have had limerick contests; numerous books of limericks have been published. Occasionally they challenge with words hard to rhyme.

Some English words seem without a rhyme. Naturally, poets have struggled to match these with accordant sound. Byron and Browning have been valiant in this quest. Witness Byron's

Ye lords of ladies intellectual,
Come tell me, have they not henpecked you all?

By combining words, by breaking words apart,

> two p-
> ennyworth of beautiful soup,

versifiers have achieved humor, or solved some of the rhyming problems.

Ask the players to make up two lines that give rhymes for any of the following words:

philosopher	velocity	widow
pilgrim	lemon	orange
garden	liquid	camel
carpet	silver	month
spirit	chimney	window

There should be some interesting combinations. The problem may be solved by running two words together, as *fat buck and thin doe* makes a match for *window*. Christina Rossetti found a rhyme with an apostrophe:

> How many weeks in a month?
> Four, as the swift moon runn'th.

Others have matched *month* by lisping. Sometimes a rhyme is achieved by deforming a word, as when Arthur Guiterman has

> the prophet Samuel
> Mounted on a camuel.

(The *camel* is a *mammal*, unless it's made of *enamel*. It's *Samuel* that is harder to rhyme.)

Bouts-Rimés, which is French for *rhymed ends,* has been a popular game since the eighteenth century. Each player writes two words that rhyme. Avoid obvious ones like *moon* and *June, gun* and *run.* Exchange papers. Each must now write a stanza (two or four lines) using these words as a rhyme. The group decides which verses are cleverest.

Rhymaway. Players write a question, preferably humorous. Papers are folded and exchanged. Without seeing the question, players write a word. Exchange papers again—no player getting one he's worked on. Now each player writes a stanza (two or four lines) answering the question and using the word as a rhyme. Question, word, and verses are read, and the group decides which is the most amusing.

Some words that will help toward amusing verses are:

chasm	motor	swagger
serpent	risible	noisy
hostess	purpose	cosmic
spectacle	nymphet	moldy
snuggle	solace	morality
motley	expire	temporary
extenuate	limit	redouble
fuddy-duddy	conspirator	urchin

For many centuries, poems have been written made up entirely of lines drawn from earlier poems. They are called centos. Favorites for such borrowing have been Homer and Virgil; among English poets, the most frequent victim has been Pope. Although these are stunts, they have mainly been serious. A more direct source of fun is to add your own line to a poet's first.

Have a number of first lines ready, or good separable single lines. You can get these by the score from any collection, such as *The Golden Treasury*. Write each on a separate sheet of paper. Give each player a line. He is to add one more line, as amusing as he can make it. Group decides which is the cleverest.

The humorist Richard Armour has written a book of these, which he calls *Punctured Poems*. Here are two:

> Tiger! Tiger! burning bright,
> What has caused you to ignite?

> A little learning is a dangerous thing,
> The drop-out muttered, leaving school last Spring.

Go thou and do likewise.

For an amateur effort, here is one of my own:

> There is a tide in the affairs of men
> That brings pollution to the shore again.

Build a Verse. Each player writes an original line. He folds the paper, and writes outside the last word of his line. Papers are exchanged. Seeing only this last word, the player who now has the paper writes another line, folds it, and writes his last word after the other last word. Exchange again, and repeat the process. The fourth player, seeing only the three last words, writes the final line of the stanza. The first three words may rhyme, but do not have to; the last word must rhyme with one of the others.

Papers are exchanged again, and read aloud. The four whose joint stanza is chosen as most amusing play again.

The Clerihew

Another rhyming stanza used exclusively for comic verse is the Clerihew, named after its originator, Edmund Clerihew Bentley. He was bored (as who has not been?) one day, and happened to be in a chemistry class, so he perpetrated this time-killer:

> Sir Humphry Davy
> Abominated gravy.
> He lived in the odium
> Of having discovered sodium.

Although he is best known as the author of the mystery *Trent's Last Case,* Bentley wrote two volumes of clerihews. Here is a political observation:

> George the Third
> Ought never to have occurred.
> One can only wonder
> At so grotesque a blunder.

And here's a scientific remark:

Sir James Jeans
Always says what he means.
He is really perfectly serious
About the Universe being mysterious.

I myself, after my fourth lexicographical venture, was caught
in a clerihew:

Joseph T. Shipley
Is a candidate for Ripley.
Believe it or not, it isn't fictionary:
He's gradually turning into a dictionary.

You will note that the clerihew has four lines; the first line
is always a name. These rhyming but irregular stanzas are not
hard to make up.

Read a few clerihews to the players, and explain their struc-
ture. In five minutes, each is to write a clerihew about someone
in the room—or about someone they all know. This may be a
personal acquaintance, like a teacher, or a public figure, like the
Vice-President.

Rhyming Pairs. Give each player a paper on which you have
written a brief phrase as a clue. He is to convert this into two
rhyming words that catch the same idea. (This is a fresh variety
of the doubling described in Chapter 7.) Here are some clues
you can give, with matching rhymes:

cowardly guy: yellow fellow
brief visit: small call
maple sugar: sweet treat
rapid ploy: quick trick
clever ploy: slick trick
delighted father: happy pappy
slight caprice: flimsy whimsy
postpone the fur: table sable
neat big top: careful hairful
get-together at noon: lunch bunch
altitude record holder: higher flier
sale of latest styles: fashion cash-in

speedy with-it boy: nippy hippie
good news: cheerful earful
lively gathering: hearty party
pretty girl stung: bitten kitten
a bad interpretation: misleading reading

You can think of more yourself. Get the rhymes first, then make the clues.

As a variation, say one clue aloud to the group. The one who gives an appropriate rhyming pair first, offers the next clue.

The pattern of rhyming couples is old and recurrent. The old fairy tale of the animals going to tell the king that the sky is falling was enacted on Broadway in the fall of 1970. Its characters are named Henny Penny, Cocky Locky, Goosey Poosey, Turkey Lurkey, and Foxy Woxy.

Haiku

Out of Japan came the Haiku, one of the simplest verse forms. It has only three lines, the first of five syllables, the second of seven, the third of five. It is used for brief description, or the fragrance of a mood. It makes a pleasant exercise in choice of words and colorful evocation. Here are four examples of the haiku:

> Mountain peaks of cloud:
> White sails, in the summer sky,
> Crowding together.

A fluttering swarm
Of cherry petals; there comes,
Driving them, the storm.

> On the lake's green bank,
> Living green, a quiet frog
> Looks with bulging eyes.

Bright flowers quiver
Over a mingled murmur:
Faces in the crowd.

Explain the five-seven-five pattern. Read an example. Then each player writes a haiku. The group discusses them, suggests improvements, decides which is most effective. The haiku has no rhyme, but it does have its reasons.

16

PROVERBS,
IMP/ROVED SAWS,
SIMPLE YET
SUBTLE SAYINGS

Proverbs, we are told, condense the wisdom of the race. But what is wisdom? Whose enthusiasm, whose caution contains the truth? Is it "Look before you leap"? Or "He who hesitates is lost"?

Charles Lamb, in a discussion of "popular fallacies," smiles at the notion that "a bully is always a coward," remarking that the observation in *Tom Brown's School Days* is closer to the truth: "Bully Dawson licked by half the town, and half the town licked by Bully Dawson."

There are other pairs of proverbs that contradict one another, as:

> A man gets no more than he pays for.
> The best things in life are free.

> Leave well enough alone.
> Progress never stands still. (If I rest, I rust.)

> The more the merrier.
> Two's company, three's a crowd.

> Out of sight, out of mind.
> Absence makes the heart grow fonder.

Make a Provergram. Scramble each word of a saying. Then change the order of the words. Mess up four in this fashion, and give them to the players. The first to straighten them out wins. Here are four provergrams:

1. rae nsight robnubts tsacf
2. gles leylb het eth recrasi
3. cause het si gruneh tbse
4. ecuas ruos veha liwl tame twese (112)

Liproverbs make another way of handling a saw. A lipogram, you remember, is writing with a letter left out. We tried this, in one way, in Chapter 4. Here is another way.

Write four proverbs, omitting all the vowels. Run the consonants together, as though they were all in one word. At the end of each, put the number of words, and a clue. Players are to separate them and restore the vowels. First to finish wins. Here are four liproverbs, with clues:

1. Dntdgyrgrvwthyrtth, 7: Try not to prepare your coffin by overeating.
2. Ncsststhtrntspl, 5: The despot says he does what he must.
3. Clmtsmnstrtchstn, 5: Misfortune really tests one.
4. Whtrdntlwwshwsnblv, 7: Our strong desires quickly fashion facts. (113)

Imp/roved Saws

The end of a proverb or common saying can often be changed, given a wry twist or unexpected turn, to shift its wisdom into humor—and still keep it true.

> "He who laughs last laughs best" may become: He who laughs last/has no sense of humor. "A watched pot never boils": A watched pot/means you're hungry.

Give an example of an imp/roved proverb. Players have three minutes to think of three well-known sayings and change their ending. The group decides which changes are cleverest. Here are a few more imp/roved sayings:

Familiarity breeds contemp/lation.
A rolling stone/may start an avalanche.
All that glisters/is loved by the girls.
A penny saved/can't buy very much.

And here is a cluster of apothegms, proverbs, sayings, aphorisms, maxims, gnomes, paroemias, adages, and saws. They are not the everyday or garden variety, but a careful culling of fresh and olden beauties. They usually mean more than they seem to say. Read them, play with them, ponder them, dispute them. In any way, enjoy them—and learn.

1. He that loses his temper is in the wrong.
2. A lawyer's suit never wears out.
3. Who speaks evil to you will speak evil of you.
4. Patience is bitter, but it bears sweet fruit.
5. The learned man knows the rules; the wise man knows the exceptions.
6. Woman is one of nature's most agreeable blunders.
7. All men think all men mortal but themselves.
8. Ole Man Know-It-All died last year.
9. It is always morning somewhere in the world.
10. Don't count on anybody but yourself—and not too much on that.
11. Who cuts his own wood warms himself twice.
12. Those that are unfit to rule yield only to violence.
13. He that bellows like a bull may be weak as a bulrush.
14. Don't fell the tree to catch the bird.
15. Happiness was born a twin.
16. Do it now, and you can spell *now* backwards.
17. It's as true as that the candle ate the cat.
18. That butterfly was a caterpillar; that dust was a butterfly.
19. Eaten bread is soon forgotten.
20. One shoe will not fit all feet.
21. Everyone blames his fault on the times.
22. He is well paid that is well satisfied.
23. The evils we bring on ourselves are the hardest to bear.
24. Pardon all but thyself.
25. Beware of the clever word that masks the unwise deed.
26. There are no fans in hell.
27. Every path has its puddle.
28. Fear has a quick ear.
29. Let patience still in your garden grow.

30. First deserve, and then desire.

31. A thousand probabilities do not make one truth.

32. A fool always rushes to the fore.

33. There is no royal road to learning.

34. Don't gaze at the moon and fall in the gutter.

35. The same knife cuts bread and fingers.

36. Good words cool more than cold water.

37. The shoe knows whether the sock has holes.

38. A hat is not made for one shower.

39. Every man is the son of his own works.

40. Hearts may agree though heads differ.

41. "They say" is half a liar.

42. Idle folk lack no excuses.

43. Thrift is a great revenue.

44. None knows the weight of another's burden.

45. The best throw of the dice is to throw them away.

46. Keeping is harder than winning.

47. Too far east is west.

48. With Latin, a horse, and money you may go far.

49. There are more ways to the wood than one.

50. A small leak will sink a great ship.

51. All lay a load on a willing horse.

52. Living well is the best revenge.

53. We may give advice but we cannot give conduct.

54. After your fling, watch for the sting.

55. No love is foul, no prison fair.

56. Although it rain, throw not away the watering pot.

57. Give losers leave to talk.

58. He that makes no mistakes makes nothing.

59. A good archer is known not by his arrows but by his aim.

60. Many things grow in the garden that were never sown.

61. Don't ask pears of the elm tree.

62. Mistrust the expected; watch for the unforeseen.

63. Men are not to be measured by inches.

64. The ass loaded with gold still eats thistles.

65. Every oak has been an acorn.

66. The busiest men have the most leisure.

67. No man loves his fetters, be they made of gold.

68. Every man is a pilot on a calm sea.

69. Every cock is proud of his own dunghill.

70. Care and diligence bring luck.

71. Little pot, soon hot.

72. Cats hide their claws.

73. Take your job seriously but not yourself.

74. Beware of fools manipulated by scoundrels.
75. A cheerful look makes a dish a feast.
76. No man is clever enough to lick his own back.
77. He that would climb the ladder must begin at the bottom rung.
78. Don't listen to one and judge two.
79. Every man has the defects of his qualities.
80. He that knoweth when he hath enough is no fool.
81. He that does you an ill turn will never forgive you.
82. Pull the child out of the water before you punish it.
83. In every country dogs will bark.
84. Eagles catch no flies.
85. Don't try to nail a shadow to the wall.
86. Worry is rust upon the blade.
87. Words have long tails.
88. There is a pedagogue called Fate; his fees are very high, and his lash heavy.
89. Many go out for wool and come home shorn.
90. The sun is never the worse for the evil it shines on.
91. A cucumber should be well sliced, and dressed with pepper and vinegar, and thrown away.
92. You cannot make an omelet without breaking eggs.
93. A man cannot whistle and drink at the same time.
94. In every country the sun rises in the morning.
95. He cannot speak well that cannot hold his tongue.
96. If the beard were all, the goat might preach.
97. It is of no use running; set out on time.
98. I wish you would explain your explanation.
99. Through a small hole one can see the sky.
100. Old men and travelers may lie by authority.
101. If you don't know where you are going, any road will take you there.
102. He is a fool that is not melancholy once a day.
103. No rope is strong enough to hang the truth.
104. Envy shoots at others and wounds herself.
105. The fish little heeds the name men give her waters.
106. Never had bad workman good tools.
107. Every ass loves to hear himself bray.
108. A barleycorn is better than a diamond, to a hen.
109. All things are difficult before they are easy.
110. He runs well, but he is off the track.
111. Slowly the ocean pounds the cliffs to sand.
112. A black hen lays a white egg.
113. It is the grace of lambs to suckle kneeling.
114. Great souls have wills; feeble ones, only wishes.
115. When I was frightened, I threatened others.

116. One must not laugh at one's own wheeze; a snuff-box has no right to sneeze.
117. Who will not look on a fool must smash his mirror.
118. He that is giddy thinks the world turns round.
119. A carefree head is found only on a scarecrow.
120. It is usually easier to suppress criticism than to meet it.
121. Habit turns a cobweb into a cable.
122. Sticks are thrown only at trees that grow fruit.
123. *L'art, c'est moi; la science, c'est nous.*
124. Between two stools my tail may go to ground.
125. Every man's reach exceeds his grasp.
126. Wherever food is, thither fly the birds.
127. A race is won at the finish line.
128. At night all cats are gray.
129. Glasses and lasses are brittle ware.
130. In whatsoever surroundings, a gem is still a gem.
131. Faults are thick where love is thin.
132. In winter, on the rose bush only the thorns remain.
133. When you are the anvil, bear; when you are the hammer, strike.
134. He is not poor that hath little, but he that desireth much.
135. Repentance comes too late.
136. Fire and pride you cannot hide.
137. The Muses love the morning.
138. Everyone thinks he has more than his share of brains.
139. He that would eat the kernel must crack the shell.
140. Don't count your chickens until you cross the bridge.
141. However far a bird may fly, it takes its tail along.
142. O Lady, we receive but what we give.
143. Hurt is the price we pay for feeling.
144. Never slam the door of your mind.
145. Better be silent and thought a fool than speak and be known one.

SOLUTIONS, ANSWERS,
WORD LISTS, AND OTHER
PARAPHERNALIA

Not all the words listed here may be in your home dictionary, but they all exist in English and can be found in the thirteen-volume *Oxford English Dictionary* or in special glossaries of science, technology, and the like.

(1) Man. As a baby, he crawls on all fours; in the noon of his strength he walks upright; in the dusk of his age he uses a cane.

(2) Children brought up in the country may recognize this: a plow.

(3) The moon, "loved" because used to foretell the future.

(4) The sun.

(5) A fly. Because in that country of crowded bazaars, as their proverb says: "Kill one fly, and a dozen come to mourn for it."

(6) Look up on a clear night for the answer: the moon amid the stars.

(7) Naturally not, for they are your own two eyes.

(8) 1. Rooster; 2. coconut; 3. nose; 4. sew; 5. eyes; 6. ear.

(9) 1. A lighted candle; 2. smoke; 3. a pair of shoes.

(10) 1. Halfway (after that, you're walking out); 2. your word; 3. none (the others fly away); 4. what does n–o–t–h–i–n–g spell? 5. an angle; 6. it knows no law; 7. a giant; 8. rock and roll.

(11) 1. The one can't see to go; the other can't go to sea.

    2. The one baits his hooks; the other hates his books.

    3. The one minds the train; the other trains the mind.

    4. The one passes the butter; the other butts the passer.

    5. He kneads (needs) the dough.

6. The cat'll (cattle) eat it.

7. Things sold at the market go to the buyer; coal goes to the cellar (seller).

(12) The ten-letter word is *homoeopath*. Here are others from the sample: atom, atop, home, hoopoe, hoot, hope, moat, moot, mope, mote, tope, toom, poom, homo, moth, oath, poem, poet, pome, tome, toph—to make more than the "twenty words, excellent" required.

(13) Coolly, knock, begin, roast. The pipe is a corncob.

(14) 1. stupid, nuance, scent, quaint: nuisance.

2. grouse, slowly, ponies, drooling: polygons.

(15) The clue words, *ice* and *pours,* add up to *precious.*

(16) Sounds like jabberwock, doesn't it? The rhymes should help you to locate the *gentle polliwog, swimming in the lake,* and the *boy kneeling, watching a garter snake.*

(17) lonely, cloud, floats, vales, hills, spied, crowd, golden daffodils.

(18) 1. live, evil, vile, veil; 2. valise, visa, verst, vast, sail; 3. leave, rivals; 4. sliver, liver, steel, veal, stave, starve; 5. slate, erase.

(19) vert, verse, verset, vest, trial, tries, strive, vase, vats, vise, valse, stir, vestal, rest, rats, rates, east, rail, rile, rive, rave, tease, reveal, lest, last, least, late, lave, arts, arse, ails, aster, averse, avert, steal, alter, ease, elate, ever, sear, sever, eaves, eves, east, eats, sere, serve, slaver, slave, elves, erst, else, elver, tale, lets, tile, tail, sate, stile, slat, slit, silt, sleet, elite, seat, steel, stale, servile, sire, steer, satire, stare, trail, stair—and there are more. The word is indeed versatile!

(20) 1. scale; 2. deceived, suspicious; 3. physicians, Diet, Quiet, Merryman; 4. teach; 5. anchor, always, water, swim; 6. loses temper, wrong; 7. facts, stubborn; 8. acorns, good, bread, baked; 9. leisure, another's, toil; 10. dances, daylight, sleep, school.

(21) 1. wards, sward; 2. dilatory, adroitly; 3. items, smite, mites, emits, me its; 4. cautioned, auctioned; 5. silent, inlets, enlist, tinsel; 6. mantel, mantle, lament; 7. enlarge, gleaner; 8. panel, penal; 9. brazier; 10. vales, salve, veals, laves; 11. praised, despair, diapers, per dais, pad sire (rise), sad pier (peri), spar die, par dies, id spear (spare); 12. sutler, luster, ulster, rustle, rulest, lurest; 13. stripe, sprite, ripest, esprit, tripes, rip set, sir pet, rep sit, res pit (tip), per its (and the word *priest* is itself actually two words, as in the sentence: "O priest, thou priest into others' affairs too much"); 14. peal, pale, plea; 15. solemn, melons; 16. repents, serpent; 17. caster, carest, recast, traces, reacts, caters, racest, carets; 18. parental, prenatal; 19. parted, prated, detrap, red apt (tap, pat), ted par; 20. pares, reaps, spare, parse, spear, rapes, asper, prase, re asp (sap); 21. acts, cast, scat; 22. warred, reward, redraw, warder; 23. respect, scepter; 24. mane, name, amen; 25. foster, softer; 26. spired, prides, redips; 27. rationalize; 28. stop, tops, spot, post; 29. cruet, recut, cuter; 30. stable, bleats, ablest, balest, be last (slat); 31. sprat, strap, traps; 32. thread, dareth, dearth; 33. meat, mate, tame; 34. stained,

detains, sainted; 35. recaps, spacer, parsec; 36. climaxes.

(22) 1. kitchen, thicken; 2. reaction, creation; 3. penetrated, repatented; 4. transpose, patroness.

(23) warts, straw.

(24)

You figure out	*You write*
1. bread	1. butter
2. thunder	2. lightning
3. Delilah	3. Samson
4. Juliet	4. Romeo
5. scrambled	5. eggs
6. Robin	6. Hood (or redbreast)

(25) 1. broken; 2. sometimes; 3. terrible; 4. annoying; 5. excellent; 6. lovely; 7. erratic. Acrostic: Beatles.

(26) 1. lazy; 2. poky; 3. easy; 4. open; 5. kindle; 6. oppose; 7. slack; 8. wander. Acrostic: slowpoke.

(27) 1. B; 2. A; 3. T; 4. P; 5. I; 6. G; 7. O (owe); 8. C; 9. J; 10. L; 11. Q; 12. U; 13. X; 14. Y; 15. M; 16. N; 17. R. There is a word *dee,* and a name Kay. There are also an *aitch*-bone (the rump of beef), a *vee* neckline, a road winding in a great *ess,* and a *zee* or *Z-bar.* E (plural) is in *ease.* Left out are only F and W—though often in betting a man will say "double you."

(28) 1. N–M–E; 2. X–S; 3. D–K; 4. I–C; 5. S–A; 6. X–L–N–C; 7. E–Z; 8. N–V; 9. X–P–D–N–C; 10. X–L; 11. I–C.

(29) She exclaimed: O–I–C–U–R–M–T!

(30) If you catch on, you can rattle it off:

> Too wise you are, too wise you be,
> I see you are too wise for me.

(31) 1. Because it's the middle of *day.*
2. Because it makes the *ear hear.*
3. Because all the others are inaudible (in <u>audible</u>).
4. Because it makes *Ma mad.*
5. *Are* becomes *area.*
6. *Ides* becomes *ideas. Came* becomes *cameo.*
7. *Smile* becomes *simile.*
8. A *teapot.*
9. Big-faced (with the *I*).

(32) Words with adjacent letters include: aba, abaca, abb, abba, baa, bacca, caaba, cabbed, cede, ceded, dee, deed, deeded, fed, fee, feed, high, mon, moon, no, noon, on, o-o, pompon, poon, poop, rusts, struts, sturts, truss, trusts, tussur, tutus.

(33) A young man of that name killed Goliath: DAVID.

(34) Read them this way:

1. I understand you undertake to overthrow my undertakings.

2. The letter was delivered to John Underhill, Andover, Massachusetts. At the beginning of World War I, the post office was instructed not to work out any more such puzzles. It still delivers letters to Santa Claus.

3. Be above quarrels between man and wife; there are faults on both sides.

4. A fond lover (A F on D, L over).

(35) 1. wrongly; 2. stupendous, hazardous, timidous, jeopardous, tremendous, but see (91); 3. falchion, stanchion; 4. scion, coercion, suspicion; 5. fashion, refashion, cushion, recushion; 6. religion, irreligion, legion, region, contagion. If you can think of more, let me know.

(36) The spelling should be:

A	B	C
1. copious	eligible	villain
2. pollute	subpoena	ecstasy
3. civility	diphthong	receiver
4. confidential	physique	abbreviate
5. regrettable	picnicking	archetype
6. triumphant	audible	bivouac
7. slovenly	ventriloquism	committed
8. strategy	sacrilegious	mutable
9. appreciate	forfeit	laryngitis
10. instigate	chieftain	seize

(37) 1. embryos; 2. taxis; 3. they (but also; there are three *it's* in the sentence); 4. the 1960's; 5. brigadier generals; 6. notaries public; 7. mesdames; 8. beaux; 9. Fannys; 10. monkeys; 11. for various kinds, moneys, for sums of money, monies. 12. ourselves; 13. alibis; 14. gallows; 15. deer; 16. for any number, fish, for different varieties, fishes; 17. genera; 18. for persons, geniuses, for spirits, genii; 19. oxen; 20. foxes; 21. titmice; 22. species; 23. inspectors general; 24. geese; 25. mongooses; 26. testatrices; 27. opera; 28. sopranos; 29. sheaves; 30. data; 31. criteria; 32. electrons; 33. amoebas, amoebae; 34. axes; 35. gross; 36. L's; 37. wolves; 38. phenomena; 39. bison; 40. fleets (fleet itself, a collective noun, may be used as either singular or plural); 41. of men, heroes, of sandwiches, heros; 42. for persons, staffs, for wood, staves; 43. larvae; 44. mosquitoes; 45. brothers, brethren; 46. passersby.

(38) foot, goose, tooth, man, woman, mouse, louse.

(39) 1. Time flies. You cannot, they fly so fast.

2. That that is, is; that that is not, is not; that that is not, is not that that is.

3. Frank, where Henry had had "had had," had had *had had;* "had had" had had the teacher's approval.

(40) What we usually call a period is also called a full stop. These lines therefore read: "If the grate be (great B) empty, put coal on (colon). If the grate be full, stop putting coal on."

(41) Here are enough for your fingers and toes: undisprovable, subordinate, undiscoverably, troublemaking, cauliflower, graciousness, authorize, consequential, tenacious, vexatious, veracious, mendacious, miscellaneous, precarious, unsociable, equation, inoculate, crematorium, auctioneer. There are many more.

(42) facetious, bacterious, abstemious, arsenious, caesious, larcenious, arterious. Yes, they all end with *ious*. Elsewhere, try to avoid the I.O.U's.

(43) French *oiseau*, which means *bird*. The tree is the *sequoia*. The cats *miaoued*.

(44) bay, bee, by, beau, boo; day, dee, die, dough, do; fay, fee, fie, foe, phew; gay, gee, guy, go, goo; hay, he, high, hoe, who; lay, lea, lie, low, loo; may, me, my, mow, moo; nay, knee, nigh, know, new; say, see, sigh, sew, sue; way, we, why, woe, woo.

(45) The mystery is solved by judicious insertions of the letter *e:*

> Persevere ye perfect men,
> Ever keep these precepts ten.

Now you can read it with ease!

(46) Have you heard these sayings? They may have deeper ideas.
1. The boughs that bear most hang lowest.
2. The higher an ape goes, the more he shows his tail.
3. Hope is as inexpensive as despair.
4. Accuracy is a duty, not a virtue.
5. The wheel that does the squeaking gets the grease.
6. The lazy dog leaned against the wall to bark.
7. Ohio; 8. Iowa; 9. health; 10. o-o; 11. Hawaii; 12. onion; 13. ukulele; 14. Europe; 15. fairy; 16. join; 17. area; 18. aerial.

(47) You should pick:
A. lb, 2c, 3a, 4b, 5c, 6b, 7a, 8d, 9d, 10d.
B. 1a, 2a, 3d, 4b, 5c, 6b, 7c, 8d, 9c, 10a.
C. 1c, 2a, 3b, 4b, 5d, 6b, 7c, 8a, 9c, 10a.
D. 1c, 2d, 3b, 4a, 5a, 6c, 7d, 8c, 9b, 10d.
E. 1d, 2b, 3c, 4a, 5a, 6d, 7c, 8b, 9a, 10c.

(48) A. 1h, 2d, 3j, 4a, 5i, 6b, 7e, 8c, 9f, 10g.
B. 1e, 2i, 3g, 4a, 5c, 6j, 7b, 8f, 9d, 10h.

(49) The double matches are: 1c, 2b, 3c, 4d.

(50) 1c. The words are opposites.
2b. Each is a frequent accompaniment.
3b. Gill and nostril are the avenues of breathing.
4b. The words are synonyms.
5b. Music and films are the fields in which each is famous.

(51) The intruders, with reasons, are:

1. *Nine* is not an even number.
2. *Frost* does not fall.

3. *Cabbage* does not grow underground.

4. *Increment* means something added, not left over.

5. All but *triangle* are solid objects, three-dimensioned.

6. *Dice* have corners not curves.

7. An *ellipse* has no corners.

8. A *woodcock* is a bird. (A woodchuck is an animal.)

9. *Feasable* is misspelled; it should be -*ible.*

10. *Tint* refers to color not odor.

11. *Minneapolis* is not a state.

12. *Meander* has no suggestion of speed.

(52) As: 1. black as coal (as pitch, as the ace of spades); 2. red as a rose (as a cherry, as blood); 3. dumb as an ox; 4. mute as a mackerel; 5. plump as a dumpling; 6. quick as a flash (as lightning); 7. thin as a rail; 8. skinny as a beanpole; 9. quiet as a mouse; 10. ugly as sin; 11. pretty as a picture; 12. pale as death; 13. white as snow (as a sheet, as a ghost); 14. sweet as sugar (as honey); 15. sour as vinegar; 16. deaf as an adder (as a post); 17. merry as a cricket (as a Greek, as mice in malt, as the day is long); 18. gay as a lark; 19. smooth as oil (as glass); 20. much sense as a hole in the wall; 21. snug as a bug in a rug; 22. innocent as a newborn babe (as a lamb); 23. fresh as a daisy (as paint); 24. pert as a sparrow; 25. tall as a lamppost; 26. high as the sky (as a kite, as an elephant's eye; of something short: high as a hog, all but the bristles); 27. long as a Welsh pedigree; 28. large as life, and twice as natural; 29. mad as a hatter (as a March hare, as Ajax); 30. spry as a kitten; 31. free as the wind (as a bird in air) 32. plenty as blackberries; 33. easy as falling off a log (as lying, as pie); 34. dry as dust (as a bone); 35. brown as a berry; 36. naked as a needle (as my nail, as a stone, as he was born); 37. brave as a lion; 38. good as gold (the French say good as bread); 39. tight as a drum; 40. right as rain (as a trivet); 41. fit as a fiddle; 42. flat as a pancake (as a flounder); 43. blind as a bat; 44. light as a feather; 45. hot as Hades; 46. cold as ice (as an icicle); 47. cool as a cucumber; 48. fat as a hog (as a bacon pig, as butter); 49. poor as a church mouse; 50. rich as a king (as Midas, as Croesus); 51. patient as Job; 52. stubborn as a mule; 53. proud as a peacock (as a pig with two tails); 54. dead as a doornail; 55. cross as two sticks; 56. angry as a wasp (as a hornet); 57. dull as dishwater; 58. plain as a pikestaff (as the nose on your face); 59. hard as a rock; 60. soft as silk; 61. clear as crystal (as a bell, as mud); 62. slippery as an eel; 63. sharp as a razor; 64. bright as a button; 65. smart as a whip; 66. clean as a whistle; 67. bald as a coot (as an egg); 68. pleased as Punch; 69. busy as a bee; 70. drunk as a lord; 71. neat as a pin; 72. ragged as a colt; 73. sound as a bell; 74. like as two peas (in a pod); 75. sure as eggs is eggs (as Fate); 76. welcome as flowers in May; 77. thick as thieves (as hail, as hops); 78. useless as monkey's fat; 79. crowded as three in a bed; 80. old as Methusaleh (as the itch).

(53) You've probably figured all these out, but in case your younger sister reads the book, here are the answers:

1. Ada is Simon's sister and his grandmother.
2. "That man" is the speaker's son.
3. The doctor is Henry's sister.
4. Anne is twelve. (Mary is twenty.) Actually, the mathematics is easy; it's the language complications that are hard. My friend the mathematical wizard Edward T. Frankel works it more simply than four books that give this classical problem. He says:

Let X equal Anne's age when Mary was three times as old as Anne, or $3x$. Note that the difference between their ages will always be $3x - x = 2x$.

When Anne is three times as old as Mary was at that time, Anne will be $9x$.

One half that is $4\frac{1}{2}x$, and when Mary was $4\frac{1}{2}x$, Anne was that minus two, or $2\frac{1}{2}x$.

Mary is now twice that, or $5x$, which means that Anne must now be $3x$.

The sum of their ages, $8x$, is 32. $x = 4$.

Therefore, Mary is now 20, and Anne is 12.

5. Philosophers have to invent a superlanguage to explain these self-contradictions.
6. If you examine this closely, you'll see that A and B cannot both be lying. Therefore C is lying, and B is telling the truth.
7. It's just too bad for Saint Paul. Everyone slips sometimes.
8. He *must* accept your invitation.
9. The stranger points in either direction, and asks: "If I were to ask you whether this is the right road to town, would you say yes?" If it's the right road, the liar, if asked, would say no; therefore he must lie now and say yes. The truther of course will say yes. Similarly, if it's the wrong road, both will say no.

   If there are several roads, the question is "Which of these roads does not lead to the town?" The truther will point to all the wrong roads; the liar will point to one road, which is therefore the right road to town.
10. Richard figured that *he* had a sure case: If he wins the suit, the court will free him from paying; if he loses, the agreement keeps him clear.

(54) A. 1c, 2c, 3b, 4d, 5b, 6d, 7a, 8b, 9a, 10c.
   B. 1b, 2a, 3a, 4c, 5b, 6c, 7d, 8d, 9a, 10b.
   C. 1b, 2a, 3d, 4c, 5d, 6a, 7b, 8c, 9a, 10b.

(55) 1. antagonize; 2. antarctic; 3. anteater; 4. anteroom; 5. antediluvian; 6. antelope; 7. A.M. (ante meridian); 8. antenna; 9. anthem; 10. anthracite;

11. anthropoid; 12. antibiotic; 13. antics; 14. antiques; 15. anticipate;
16. anticlimax; 17. anticlockwise; 18. antidote; 19. antipathy; 20. an-
tipodes; 21. antiquary; 22. antiquated; 23. antonym; 24. antithesis.

(56) 1. refuse′, ref′use, re′-fuse′; 2. supplȳ′, sup′plȳ; 3. tier (ē, twice), ti′er;
4. worsted (oost, urst); 5. hĭnder, hīnder; 6. tears (ē, ā); 7. wound (au,
oo); 8. mīnute′, mĭn′ute; 9. number (second and third *b* silent); 10. sow
(ō, au); 11. does (duz, doze); 12. prĭmer, prīmer; 13. en′trance, en-
trance′; 14. lead (ē, ĕ), row (ō, au).

(57) A. 1. sold, soled; 2. prays, praise, preys; 3. peer, pier; 4. eyes, ayes; 5.
son, sun; 6. reins, rains; 7. sow, so, sew; 8. quire, choir; 9. way, weigh,
whey; 10. sweet, suite.

B. 1. climes, climbs; 2. one, won; 3. stares, stairs; 4. wet, whet; 5. bows,
boughs; 6. canons, cannons; 7. steel, steal; 8. insight, incite; 9. allowed,
aloud; 10. rays, raze, raise.

(58) 1. America; 2. ammonia, chemical from the urine of the camels waiting
outside his temple at Siwa, while his believers prayed inside; 3. atlas,
Atlantic Ocean; 4. cereal; 5. the German *Thaler,* our dollar; 6. guillo-
tine, replacing the headsman's ax; 7. a hamburger is a chopped meat
patty, usually of beef; because the first syllable accidentally is the word
for *cured pork,* other words, like *beefburger* and *cheeseburger,* have
also come into use; 8. iridescent, the iris of the eye, iridium; 9. Julius
Caesar reformed the reckoning of the year with the Julian calendar;
July is named after him, also the *Caesarean section,* the way he was
(supposedly) born, also *kaiser* and *czar;* 10. because July was given
thirty-one days Augustus, the adopted son and successor of Julius, was
granted thirty-one days also for August, the month named after him;
11. saxhorn, saxtuba, saxophone; 12. volcano, vulcanize; 13. frank-
furter; 14. the month of March, martial, also the planet Mars, whence
the Martians; 15. limousine (first a fine carriage, then a fine car).

(59) 1. a river in Asia Minor; 2. Bayonne, France; 3. Taranto, Italy; 4.
Hector, a champion of Troy, son of Priam; slain by Achilles; 5. Mrs.
Amelia Bloomer, American, wore them in the 1850's; 6. Brundisium,
Italy; 7. Croatia, Austria (now in Yugoslavia); 8. Cupid, blind young
Roman god of desire; 9. Corinth, Greece; 10. Armenia, now part of the
Soviet Union; 11. Hermes, messenger of the Greek gods; 12. Jove,
another name for Jupiter, king of the Roman gods; 13. Magnesia, in
Turkey (where the Romans defeated Antiochus the Great in 190 B.C.);
14. Marcel Grateau, nineteenth-century French hairdresser; 15. Mary
Magdalene, in the Bible, who repented and wept; 16. Port Mahón,
Minorca (a Mediterranean island off Spain); 17. from Milan; 18. Orcus,
Roman god of Tartarus, the place of torment; 19. Pan, Greek god of
nature; being everywhere, *pan* means all, hence *pandemonium, pana-
cea, pan-American,* etc.; 20. Don Quixote, in book by Spanish writer
Miguel de Cervantes, 1605; 21. John Montague, Earl of Sandwich,
gambled lengthily; instead of leaving the gaming table he had meat

brought to him between slices of bread; 22. *Espagnol,* the French word for Spaniard; 23. Spanish greens; 24. Tangier, Morocco; 25. prunus Persica, the Persian fruit.

(60) 1. Dutch auction: auctioneer begins by announcing a high figure, which he gradually reduces until somebody bids; 2. Dutch anchor: something essential forgotten or left behind; 3. Dutchman's breeches: a small patch of blue in a stormy sky; 4. Dutch bargain: one clinched over liquor—trying to get the other man drunk and befuddled so as to take advantage of him; 5. Dutch comfort: Thank God it was no worse! 6. Dutch courage: supplied by liquor; 7. Dutch defense: surrender; 8. Dutch feast: one at which the host gets drunk before his guests; 9. Dutch gold: an alloy of copper and zinc, a cheap imitation of gold leaf; 10. Dutch luck: undeserved good fortune; 11. Dutch nightingale: a frog; 12. Dutch concert: everyone plays a different tune; 13. Dutch praise: seeming praise that belittles; 14. Dutch reckoning: a lump sum —higher than it would be if itemized; 15. Dutch wife: a pillow between the legs (to absorb perspiration) in tropical climes; 16. talk like a Dutch uncle: to speak bluntly, to scold roundly; 17. I'll be a Dutchman: I'm damned; 18. in Dutch: in trouble, in disfavor; 19. double Dutch: gibberish; 20. Dutchman's land: "Cape Flyaway," a fog or cloud on the horizon that looks like land.

(61) A. 1. manna; 2. manuscript; 3. manhole; 4. many; 5. manhunt; 6. mania; 7. mansion; 8. mango; 9. manhood; 10. manicure.

B. 1. program; 2. probable; 3. probe; 4. problem; 5. proceed; 6. prohibit; 7. professor; 8. pronounce; 9. prophet; 10. propose.

(62) 1. admit, admired, adroit, adamant, address, added, admittance, advantage; 2. Beatles, beg, belittle, Beethoven, because, believe, best, beautiful, beloved, belong; 3. perhaps, permit, person, persists, peering, persuasive, personality, perform; 4. contain, contempt, contract, convoy, consignment, confuse, conducted, congratulated, consul; 5. intended, interfere, investigation, inquiries, interested, inquest, into.

(63) Here are just a few:

wring	slight	sliver	steal	cluck
click	clung	cluster	flitter	flatter
lapse	ideal	dalliance	meager	rankle
lark	lash	delves	shire	shut
sill	broad	praise	brow	shovel
close	plain	bright	crack	player
craven	crock	stile	stinker	gloom
function	stumble	shackles	stipple	president
cache	player	least	learn	leaves

Also: *revolution* (good change!) and *slaughter* (note the happy change from *manslaughter* to *man's laughter*). And: *hare, hair, hale, hail, ham, hart, hate, hat, have, hit, hoar, height, hear.*

(64)

trope	terror	tone	trod
troll	trip	thick	tripe
tape	twit	twitch	twine
trough	taught	tale	till
teach	tall	teasel	trap
tail	town	taunt	thorn
turn	tangle	table	touch
trite	taxis	then	task
train	tend	trend	treason
those	tramp	travel	trifle
tour	trice	trill	theft
trick	thence	tether	trouble
trim	testate	trip	their
that	tease		

(65)

shave	blowing	place	scram*	meat
still	stray*	eastern*	aloft	growing*
trail	slit	stale	cleaves*	about
women*	spark	cheat*	swarm	slate
snail	amuse	price	spear	preach
craft	crave	brave	slave	grasp
clash	grope	slope	trope	score*
there*	where*	scream		

*Can be beheaded three times, making four words.

(66) Here are the original words:

A 1. grime; 2. sliver; 3. small; 4. maim; 5. scope; 6. scone; 7. scoop; 8. slight; 9. slow; 10. clamp.

B 1. trifle; 2. trump; 3. tact; 4. tangle; 5. truffle; 6. touch; 7. tone; 8. tread; 9. treason; 10. task.

C 1. scowl; 2. adrift; 3. agape; 4. apart; 5. trash; 6. spore; 7. sledge; 8. trace; 9. trend; 10. scat.

(67) sparkling, sparking, sparing, spring, sprig, prig, pig, pi, I.

(68) 1. William Shakespeare; 2. Winston Churchill; 3. Franklin Delano Roosevelt; 4. Florence Nightingale; 5. Babe Ruth; 6. Charlie Chaplin; 7. Abraham Lincoln; 8. Adolf Hitler; 9. Albert Einstein; 10. Pablo Picasso; 11. Mao Tse-tung; 12. Neil Armstrong.

(69) Here are a few of the host of possibilities to ponder, or to make your own clues for more gaming:

brook	bronze	fraction	pleasant	brunt
glum	grill	trout	breaker	clement
blank	bland	courtly	friction	fright
mean	shingle	cramp	place	slight
bride	stimulate	scent	supine	swag

swear	drawn	through	thrash	trick
drear	trickle	wrench	swore	tropics
swallow	wriggle	trowel	stolid	bluff
gnash	steam	staid	brawl	flare
black	blind	groat		

Original words, clued: 1. bleach; 2. brought; 3. skeptic; 4. stung; 5. drunk; 6. drown; 7. gravel; 8. stag; 9. scandal; 10. grave; 11. brother; 12. stable.

(70)

hope	corn	torn	worn	batted	part	cart
hart	mart	harp	germ	tern	fern	burn
turn	gamy	pant	lent	bent	pint	hint
sent	went	cant	rant	lint	main	rain
fain	wain	hear	salt	malt	halt	cord
poured	colt	dolt	melt	belt	soup	cream
cast	fast	mast	past	card	bard	hard
ward	carp	goat	coat	poet	rote	bead
feed	lead	read	said	weed	waisted	basted
about	hilt	silt	wilt	kiln	comma	cost
host	lost	post	pelt	weld	harm	cause
axle	band	hand	manned	panned	sand	wand
coast	chain	cheat	chief	cold	cosy	

Clued words: 1. steep; 2. varnish; 3. consign; 4. mental; 5. mendication; 6. haste; 7. float; 8. kilt; 9. cinder; 10. copy; 11. clean; 12. baby; 13. cheap; 14. morose; 15. groin; 16. louse; 17. resin; 18. holly; 19. weed; 20. created; 21. dream; 22. sprite; 23. berater; 24. shriver.

(71) Here are a few, which you may clue:

starting	plain	claim	cruise	scream
clout	shout	boast	cloud	plaster
trout	shiver	steam	badge	slant
planted	basis	bathe	swarm	chaffing
caste	chair	waisted	coast	prized
blend	grind	crimes	spurn	corpse
brakes	spiked	sport	sliver	manage
packing	annuals	mantilla		

Original words, clued: 1. scarred; 2. chart; 3. barber; 4. shamming; 5. braid; 6. scoured; 7. corked; 8. lambing; 9. tamper; 10. started; 11. beard; 12. carat; 13. batch; 14. beast; 15. coast; 16. carve; 17. chirp; 18. clamp; 19. scant; 20. poster; 21. plaint; 22. parting; 23. brain; 24. witch.

(72) Here are some buried words, for which you can make clues:

bleed	claws	flashy	start	magenta	white
thumb	stage	sacred	trunk	praised	speak.
groves	pledges	narrows	chasten	weights	lottery

cleanse	triter	against	plunger	oration	crusts
centers	seventh	sampler	thorns	pirates	slumbery
grows	emerged	boils	honey	valet	cloth
flamed	whist	peony	daily	pitchy	stark
chasm	brought	salient	party	severe	haughty
glade	facet	dairy	plenty	fabled	grounds
irate	knight	keels	enamel		

Clued words (buried word inside): 1. bairn; 2. fired; 3. grunt; 4. shame; 5. spine; 6. wrath; 7. beard; 8. alien.

(73) reputation, deputation, put, dispute, computer, putative, putty, computations.

(74) a, at, ate, late, elate, relate, prelate, prelates.

flotsam, floats, float, foal, oaf, of, O.
spaniels, spaniel, panels, plane, pane, nap, an, a (plan, pan, an, a).
cheaters, teaches, cheats, teach, heat, ate (hat), at, a.
chosen, cones, cone, one, on, O (hosen, hone, hoe, ho, O).
drowned, wonder, drown, down, own (don), on (do), O.
sprouted, sported, poster, trope, port, tor, or, O (pot, to, O).

I, it, tie, rite, inter, retain, certain, reaction, cremation, importance.
(75) Here are a few, to ponder or make clues:

hot/house	book/worm	dead/head	sweet/meat
clap/trap	black/jack	medal/lion	pile/driver
cur/rant	cur/rent	end/less	red/den
under/mine	water/log	gent/eel	short/hand
high/ball	half/wit	for/mat	for/swear
tact/less	for/sake	of/ten	gang/way
gar/den	gar/net	grid/iron	fur/below
fore/shorten	four/score	fore/lock	uncle/an
fore/close	pat/tern	gun/metal	neigh/boring
bar/king	plea/sure	contra/sting	false/hood
par/rot			

Clued words: 1. bag/pipe; 2. board/walk; 3. buoy/ant; 4. port/ray; 5. hood/wink; 6. for/tune; 7. forth/right; 8. check/room; 9. way/laid; 10. in/tact; 11. critic/ally; 12. cur/tail.

(76) (a) therein: the, there, herein, he, her, here, ere, re, rein, in.
(b) seven: even, eve. (c) ushers: us, she, he, her, hers.

(77) 1.

```
pa |n| ts
 e |r| ase
den|o| ted
  a|g| round
   |w| hen
  grown
```

2.

```
   |b| lame
  b|l| ank
 ch|i| ef
 fa|c| t
  s|m| ack
  climb
```

3.

```
clas|p| s
   h|e| aven
  re|a| d
   s|c| andal
   t|h| ick
  cheap
```

(78) 1.

disc	l	aim
war	e	house
now	a	days
back	g	round
belie	v	able

gavel

2.

far	m	yard
cable	g	ram
art	i	choke
bull	e	tin
cent	r	ally

grime

3.

tea	r	drop
scar	e	crow
she	a	the
sap	p	hire
gun	s	hot

spear

(79) A. state   B. delay   C. repay
       aster   adept   dream
       caste   adder   cores
       crest   blade   stare
       smart   drone   rinse

(80) Tuck in:

1. idle; 2. dead; 3. rule; 4. rest; 5. ramble; 6. tombs; 7. male; 8. is; 9. round; 10. rim; 11. cut; 12. lit; 13. rascal; 14. tug; 15. part; 16. mart; 17. revolt; 18. sated; 19. hotel; 20. face; 21. see; 22. fiction; 23. apt; 24. lie; 25. can (tin is also there, if you prefer what they call it in England); 26. urge; 27. last; 28. vacate; 29. pinned; 30. rage; 31. debate; 32. sue; 33. slid; 34. sin; 35. superior; 36. mates; 37. tries; 38. cue; 39. ruin; 40. poses; 41. sons; 42. tainted; 43. union; 44. partly; 45. barred; 46. elation; 47. unity; 48. completed.

(81) 1. mishap pleased: apple; 2. end a tension: date; 3. little money: lemon; 4. If I get: fig; 5. hope a charmer: peach; 6. big rap every: grape; 7. ape arranges: pear; 8. buffalo ran generally: orange.

(82) 1. warder; 2. star; 3. emit; 4. net; 5. door; 6. gnat; 7. stressed; 8. step; 9. edit; 10. rail; 11. ram; 12. rebut.

(83) Here are the twin ends: 1. al; 2. ing; 3. res; 4. ent; 5. le; 6. ent; 7. sh; 8. ph; 9. es; 10. sh; 11. ed; 12. ing.

(84) 1. redder; 2. deified; 3. refer; 4. level; 5. eke; 6. noon; 7. tenet; 8. reviver; 9. tot; 10. minim; 11. deed; 12. civic; 13. repeeper; 14. gag.

(85) Here are my Crow Flights; perhaps you can beat them: pig-wig-wag-sag-say-sty; ship-skip-skid-said-sail; sin-son-won-woe (a quick journey!); hate-have-lave-love; hand-band-bond-fond-food-foot; black-slack-stack-stalk-stale-shale-whale-while-white; try-wry-way-wan-win; safe-sale-sole-hole-home; less-loss-lose-lore-more.

(86) 1. cloth-bloom; 2. trust-crust; 3. blind-climb; 4. believe-trained; 5. concern-discord; 6. platitude-condiment; 7. resigning-designate.

(87) 1. bad, don, day, mad; 2. par, rat, raw, mar; 3. set, tea, ton, mat; 4. lie, end, eat, bee; 5. con, now, nap, ban; 6. say, yes, you, try.

(88)

S	L	A	M
L	A	M	A
A	M	E	N
M	A	N	Y

D	E	A	R
E	L	S	E
A	S	P	S
R	E	S	T

P	O	S	T
O	B	O	E
S	O	O	N
T	E	N	T

R	E	N	D
E	R	I	E
N	I	C	E
D	E	E	R

T	I	D	E
I	D	E	A
D	E	A	R
E	A	R	S

(89)

S	P	O	R	T
P	A	C	E	R
O	C	H	R	E
R	E	R	U	N
T	R	E	N	D

P	A	R	T	S
A	B	O	U	T
R	O	U	T	E
T	U	T	O	R
S	T	E	R	N

B	E	A	C	H
E	N	U	R	E
A	U	G	E	R
C	R	E	E	D
H	E	R	D	S

C	H	A	N	T
H	O	M	E	R
A	M	U	S	E
N	E	S	T	S
T	R	E	S	S

S	P	A	C	E
P	A	G	A	N
A	G	E	N	T
C	A	N	O	E
E	N	T	E	R

(90) Regular alphabet: fag, bag, gab, no, chide, hide, joins, not, nuts, stun, chintz, joints, in, Styx, stunts, tunic, him, hints, ton, tun, on, stonied, dime, mint, jots, din, died, did, noon, chin, snot, dint, hid, id, union, ion, onion, sty, hie, stout, snide, snout, out, chic, gaff, mid, mini, minim, hic, chino.

Boustrophedon: bilk, milt, bills, kills, mills, hills, forms, nor, bails, aims, fed, kilts, for, chill, him, slim, fop, fog, go, of, off, jilts, jab, jail, limns, jib, kilts, ails, snory, prog, prof, proof, prong, feed, pronged, edge, noon, on, no, gong, milk, pop, prop, poop, snoop, snoopy, gory, fogged, goofed, goof, gee, nogg, pongee, goons, goop, chic.

(91) timidous, stupendous, jeopardous, tremendous, hazardous. If you want to get technical, you may add vanadous, molybdous, mucidous, multifidous, frondous, decapodous, lagopodous, steganopodous, heteropodous, gasteropodous, isopodous, ligniperdous. To give any more would be nefandous.

(92) 1. shun; 2. position; 3. coercion; 4. version; 5. cushion; 6. connexion; 7. falchion; 8. luncheon; 9. passion; 10. ocean; 11. musician; 12. Russian. For good measure, there is the man that lives near the equator, so that his shadow falls sometimes north, sometimes south: He is an *amphiscian*. And Paul wrote a message (now in the Bible) to every Christian Galatian.

(93) Add the *s* to: 1. cares; 2. as; 3. princes; 4. cables; 5. needles; 6. handles; 7. ogres; 8. asses; 9. his; 10. pus.

(94) Here are the full words: 1. plum/met; 2. car/nation; 3. fat/her; 4. nap/kin; 5. far/row; 6. sin/us; 7. slit/hers; 8. tot/ally; 9. to/aster; 10. pig/eon; 11. whim/per; 12. miss/ion; 13. die/titian; 14. on/us; 15. plan/gent; 16. law/fully.

(95) A. 1. mistake; 2. fortune; 3. curtail; 4. mastiff.
B. 1. planets; 2. spinose; 3. cornice; 4. burnous.
C. 1. martens; 2. castile; 3. tartars; 4. sorties.

(96) A. 1. cat; 2. bat; 3. cut; 4. but; 5. get; 6. set; 7. hit; 8. lit; 9. lot; 10. not.
B. 1. mug; 2. log; 3. sag; 4. rag; 5. jig; 6. tug; 7. fog; 8. beg; 9. big; 10. leg.

(97) 1. Mend? I can't! (mendicant); 2. Imp lied (implied); 3. Art? I choke! (artichoke); 4. As he sat a light (satellite); 5. Taint!; 6. In gray she ate (ingratiate).

(98) 1. aspiration; 2. preparation; 3. separation; 4. vituperation; 5. perspira-

tion; 6. administration; 7. arbitration; 8. illustration; 9. enumeration; 10. refrigeration; 11. gyration; 12. oration.

(99) *Animation* has an *m*, not an *n*. *Consternation* is repeated.

(100) 1. advice; 2. slice; 3. avarice; 4. prejudice; 5. jaundice; 6. cockatrice; 7. trice; 8. device; 9. twice; 10. dice; 11. spice; 12. precipice.

(101) 1. championship; 2. hardship; 3. friendship; 4. censorship; 5. citizenship; 6. ownership; 7. warship; 8. dictatorship; 9. courtship; 10. sportsmanship; 11. chairmanship; 12. marksmanship.

(102) 1. lake; 2. drake; 3. headache; 4. rake; 5. snake; 6. awake; 7. forsake; 8. fake; 9. earthquake; 10. cake; 11. brake; 12. shake.

(103) 1. lemonade, limeade; 2. weighed; 3. mermaid; 4. accolade; 5. afraid; 6. jade; 7. marmalade; 8. shade; 9. centigrade; 10. cannonade; 11. brade; 12. persuade; 13. jade.

(104) 1. abdicate; 2. candidate; 3. sophisticate; 4. syndicate; 5. elucidate; 6. inundate; 7. vindicate; 8. invalidate; 9. dilapidate; 10. delicate; 11. masticate; 12. sedate; 13. lubricate; 14. advocate; 15. liquidate; 16. consolidate; 17. domesticate; 18. prevaricate; 19. duplicate; 20. intimidate; 21. predate; 22. confiscate; 23. depredate; 24. intoxicate.

(105) 1. subjugate; 2. expurgate; 3. segregate; 4. variegate; 5. conjugate; 6. corrugate; 7. promulgate; 8. circumnavigate; 9. investigate; 10. castigate; 11. interrogate; 12. aggregate.

(106) *-ce*: dace, face, lace, mace, pace, race, tace, bice, dice, lice, mice, nice, pice, rice, sice, vice, luce, puce, once, syce;

-de: bade, cade, fade, hade, jade, lade, made, wade, cede, rede, bide, fide, hide, nide, ride, side, tide, vide, wide, bode, code, lode, mode, node, rode, dude, nude, rude;

-ke: bake, cake, fake, hake, lake, make, rake, sake, take, wake, bike, dike, hike, like, mike, Nike, pike, tike, coke, joke, poke, woke, yoke, duke, puke;

-le: bale, dale, gale, hale, kale, male, pale, rale, sale, tale, vale, wale, able, dele, ogle, Yale, bile, file, mile, Nile, pile, rile, sile, tile, vile, wile, bole, cole, dole, hole, mole, pole, role, sole, vole, mule, pule, rule, Yule, orle, isle, axle;

-me: came, dame, fame, game, hame, lame, Mame, name, same, tame, acme, deme, dime, lime, mime, rime, time, come, dome, home, mome, Nome, pome, Rome, some, tome, fume, Hume, cyme;

-ne: bane, cane, Dane, fane, jane, lane, mane, pane, rane, sane, tane, vane, wane, dene, gene, mene, bine, kine, dine, fine, line, mine, nine, pine, sine, tine, vine, wine, bone, cone, done, gone, hone, lone, none, pone, tone, zone, dune, lune, rune, tune, erne, June, dyne, eyne, syne;

-re: bare, care, dare, fare, hare, mare, pare, rare, tare, ware, yare, acre, cere, here, mere, sere, were, ogre, eyre, byre, dire, fire, gyre, hire, lyre, mire, pyre, sire, tire, tyre, wire, bore, core, fore, gore, lore, more, pore, sore, tore, wore, yore, cure, dure, lure, mure, pure, sure;

-se: base, case, vase, ease, rise, vise, wise, dose, hose, lose, nose, pose, rose, fuse, muse, ruse, bise, else, apse, Erse, lese (majesty);

-te: bate, cate, date, fate, gate, hate, late, mate, pate, rate, sate, fete, mete, Pete, rete, bite, cite, mite, rite, kite, site, ante, cote, dote, mote, note, pote, rote, tote, vote, cute, jute, lute, mute;

-nt: cant, pant, rant, bent, cent, dent, fent, gent, kent, lent, rent, sent, tent, vent, went, ain't, dint, hint, lint, mint, pint, tint, vint, font, wont, aunt, bunt, hunt, lunt, punt, runt;

-rt: cart, dart, fart, hart, mart, part, tart, pert, vert, wert, airt, dirt, girt, bort, fort, mort, port, tort, wort, curt, hurt;

-st: bast, cast, fast, hast, last, mast, oast, past, vast, best, gest, hest, jest, lest, nest, pest, rest, test, vest, west, zest, cist, fist, gist, list, mist, wist, cost, dost, host, lost, most, post, erst, bust, dust, fust, gust, just, lust, must, oust, rust, cyst.

(107) 1. rightly (lea); 2. mattress; 3. earthquake; 4. mandate; 5. rumpus; 6. written; 7. quicksand; 8. soapstone; 9. sweepstake (steak); 10. improve; 11. madam (A.M.); 12. asset; 13. increase; 14. lock; 15. badinage.

(108) *Ch* pronounced *k*: chyme, chyle, chrysanthemum, chrysalid, chronicle, chromosome, chronic, chromatic, etc., christen and Christmas, etc., chiasmic, chimera, chiromancy, chiropractor, etc., chitin, chiton, chloride, etc., chloroform, chlorophyll, chrism, choir, chameleon, cholera, etc., chalcedony, chronometer, cholesterol, character, etc., chaotic, chorus, etc., charisma, chasm, chela, chemical, etc., Chianti, chord, chiaroscuro.

    Ch pronounced *sh*: chiffon, chignon, chiffonier, chivalry, etc., chaise longue, chanty, chagrin, chalet, chassis, chef, chemise, chamois, chartreuse, chauffeur, chute, champagne, charlotte (russe etc.), chauvinism, etc., chandelier, charlatan, chateau, chatelain, chaperon, charabanc, charade, charivari, cheroot, chenille, chargé d'affaires, cheval glass, chevalier, chevron, chic, chicanery, chichi.

    It almost looks as though *ch* pronounced as *ch* is an exception! Even though the church mouse chews cheese.

(109) tough (uff); through (oo); though (long o); ought (aw); cough (awf); plough (au); thorough (light o); hough (ock); *slough* may be *oo, au,* or *uff,* according to the meaning.

(110) Long *o*: whoa, sew, doe, owe, brooch, although, blow, oh, soul, es-

quimau, bureau, curaçao, pharaoh, depot, yeoman, apropos, go, *de trop.*

Add names, and there are Rochefoucauld, Voeux, Bordeaux, Vaux, Prevost, Gounod, Perrault, Tussaud, Keogh.

Long *u*: few, debut, beauty, Q, feud, accrue, queue, adieu, view, you, yule, use, ewe, ragout. French *nous.*

Long *e*: be, bee, beam, conceit, people, key, quay, gasoline, piece, phoenix, debris, lea. Leigh, Caesar.

s: cent, say, psychology, scent, miss, nice, answer, schism.

sh: shun, position, coercion, tension, special, specious, cushion, sugar, connexion, pshaw, schist, falchion, luncheon, nauseous, passion, ocean, musician, conscience, expatiate, eschscholtzia. Russian, Galatian.

t: cut, kissed, butt, butte, right, site, debt, ctenoid, ptarmigan, phthisic. Thomas.

(111) Queue.
(112) 1. Facts are stubborn things.
    2. The belly carries the legs.
    3. Hunger is the best sauce.
    4. Sweet meat will have sour sauce.
(113) 1. Don't dig your grave with your teeth.
    2. Necessity is the tyrant's plea.
    3. Calamity is man's true touchstone.
    4. What ardently we wish we soon believe.

INDEX